I
A

Industrial Archaeology

A SERIES EDITED BY
L. T. C. ROLT

4

The Textile Industry

An account of the early inventions of
spinning, weaving, and knitting machines

The Textile Industry

An account of the early inventions of
spinning, weaving, and knitting machines

W. English, M.Sc.Tech., F.T.I.

Longmans

LONGMANS, GREEN AND CO LTD

London and Harlow
*Associated companies, branches, and representatives
throughout the world*

© *Walter English 1969*
First published 1969

To My Wife

*Printed in Great Britain
by W & J Mackay & Co Ltd, Chatham*

Contents

List of Illustrations

facing page

PLATES

vii

DRAWINGS IN TEXT

Preface

Writings on industrial and economic history may be divided broadly into two classes: those which describe the effects of inventions and their development on the social and economic scene, and those which describe these inventions in technical detail. The former usually refer to the inventions in somewhat vague terms, and occasionally give erroneous descriptions, while the latter are often full of technical details and terms not easily understood by the general reader.

I have taken a course between these extremes and have tried to show how the early inventors transferred manual operations to mechanical ones, and to explain in as few technical terms as possible how the machines worked and how they were later developed to influence the progress of the Industrial Revolution. It is one which should appeal to many in this technological age.

This historical-technical approach should also be of interest not only to those concerned with history in general but also to those who are beginning the study of the textile industry as it is today.

To readers wishing to keep in touch with current information on historic matters concerning the textile industry, I would mention that there is a Historic Section of the Textile Institute whose members are actively engaged in collecting information, and in endeavouring to preserve old mills, machines, and records relating to textiles. One important activity is that of using such old mills as are preserved as museums for the housing of early machines. Bulletins are issued from time to time to members supplying information about these mills and their situations, as well as other information of historic interest. The Section staff have collected the information which has enabled me to compile the list of museums with textile exhibits to be found in the Appendix.

Finally, my thanks are due to those who have supplied me with valuable information and assistance in the writing of this book. They include the Textile Institute, the Manchester Central Library, especially the librarians of the Historical, Reference, Technical and Patents Sections, and many very helpful librarians and curators of public libraries and museums throughout the country.

CHAPTER ONE

The Two Wheels

The earliest successful multiple-spindle spinning machines were
inspired by and developed from the domestic spinning wheels, of
which there were two distinct types. It will therefore be easier to
understand the working of the machines if an explanation of the
wheels and their operation is given first.

The wheels in turn were developed from the spindle method of
spinning, this being the first step towards the mechanisation of the
spinning process, a process which converts fibrous materials such as
wool, flax, and cotton into threads technically known as yarns.

The spindle method consisted in either resting the spindle in a
vertical position on a suitable support or 'bearing' or suspending it
in mid-air by the thread being spun. In either case, each length of
thread spun was then wrapped or wound on to the spindle—in early
times a short stick. A notch at the top of the spindle served to hold
the thread during the spinning. The wool or other material to be
spun was held on a larger stick, termed a distaff, and the spinster
drew her supplies from this, holding a small tuft of fibres which
extended to the suspended thread. At intervals with her other hand
she gave the spindle a twirl, and as the spindle rotated it inserted
twist into the thread. This twist laid the fibres in spiral formation and
compressed them together until a relatively strong thread resulted.
The action is readily understood by reference to Fig. 1, in which S is
the spindle, W the previously spun thread wound on the spindle,
T the thread being spun and N the notch. A disc D on the spindle
acts as a flywheel, giving out stored energy and so reducing the fre-
quency of the twirling action. By the suspended-spindle method,
skilled spinsters were often able to carry on their spinning even
when walking along the roads:

> And many yet adhere,
> To the ancient distaff at the bosom fix'd,
> Casting the whirling spindle as they walk.[1]

It was the discovery or invention of the application of the wheel to turn the spindle which became the first step leading to the invention of the spinning jenny, many centuries later.

Figure 1 Spinning
by the suspended spindle

The Earlier Spinning Wheel

It is not known when or where the spinning wheel was first used, but it is believed to have originated in the East. It is possible that it was first used as a winding device in the processing of silk and, if this was so, it would soon be found that it could be used to twist the silk as well.

The spindle was positioned horizontally and supported by bear-

1 (Above) The old spinning
   wheel—drawing-out,
   twisting and winding

2 (Left) An old stocking
   frame

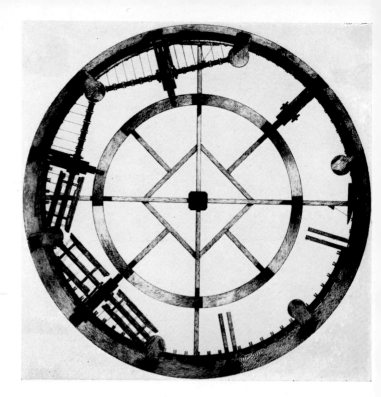

3
Lombe's silk-
throwing
machine-plan

4
Lombe's
silk-throwing
machine—
elevation

ings, and was rotated through a driving band or cord from a large wheel also held in bearings, the whole forming one framework for both spindle and wheel. The actual spinning operation is shown in

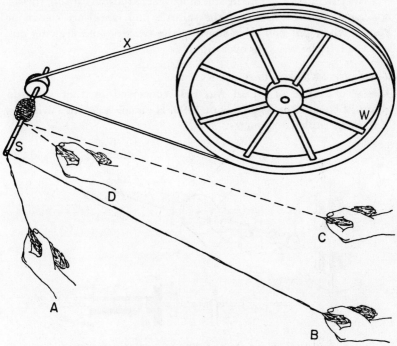

Figure 2 Spinning and winding on the old wheel

Fig. 2, the framework being omitted for clarity. The twisting and drawing-out processes are shown at A and B, where the spinster holds the spinning thread at an obtuse angle with the spindle, causing the thread to be wound spirally along the spindle and then to begin slipping off the end of the spindle, so inserting twist in the length held by the spinster, the notch in the spindle no longer being needed. At the same time, the spinster releases more fibres and moves her hand further from the spindle, so drawing out the thread to the required fineness. When the length is completed she moves her hand to hold the thread approximately at right angles to the spindle, as shown at C, and winds the thread on to the spindle. The process is repeated until the spindle is filled. It was often the practice,

after the twisting process and before winding, to turn the spindle a
few revolutions in the reverse direction to remove the spiral coils
on the spindle, so that when later the thread was unwound there
was less risk of entanglement and of excessive tension causing thread
breakages. General views of the spinster and wheel are shown in
Plate 1, the right-hand side showing the twisting and drawing out
and the left the winding operations.

The Later Spinning Wheel
The second type of wheel was first conceived by that versatile
genius, Leonardo da Vinci, about 1490. He made a detailed drawing
of it, with explanatory notes.

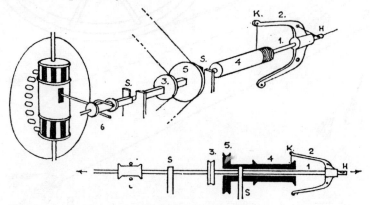

Figure 3 Leonardo da Vinci's spinning wheel (above) Jurgen's
wheel (below)

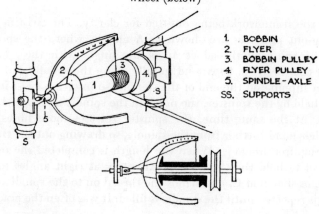

1. BOBBIN
2. FLYER
3. BOBBIN PULLEY
4. FLYER PULLEY
5. SPINDLE-AXLE
SS. SUPPORTS

About the year 1530 Jurgens of Brunswick constructed a wheel similar in principle to that of Leonardo, and a description of this will also serve for the earlier invention. Both inventors arranged the wheel to be hand turned, but subsequently either Jurgens or a later inventor added a crank and treadle to enable the spinster to turn the wheel with her foot. This left both hands free to manipulate the fibres being spun. The fundamental difference between the older wheel and the ones Leonardo and Jurgens devised lay in the provision of a 'flyer' and a bobbin as well as a spindle. The flyer was U-shaped and revolved with the spindle. It was known and used several centuries before Leonardo's time, although its function was somewhat different (see Chapter 3). Leonardo may have known of this flyer, and Jurgens, too, probably knew of either the earlier one or of Leonardo's. Fig. 3 shows perspective views of Leonardo's (above)

Figure 4 The Saxony wheel

and Jurgen's arrangements, Fig. 4 a general view of the whole of the latter type of wheel, of which there were many variations in structure as between one country and another[2] and Fig. 5 a side view of the flyer spindle and bobbin. The distaff or rock is shown attached to the framework, and holding a mass of fibres. The spinster removed a tuft of these fibres and fed them to the twisting yarn by one of two methods which are described later in this chapter, at the same time turning the wheel through the treadle. Unlike the spinster using the older wheel, however, she also slackened her hold on the yarn to allow it to be wound on to the bobbin as it was being twisted.

The yarn F next passed through a hole at the end of the flyer A (Fig. 5), down a leg of the flyer, round one of the hooks G and on to the bobbin D. A driving cord from the wheel passed round pulleys C and E on the spindle B and on the bobbin, and as the pulley on the bobbin was smaller, so the bobbin revolved at a higher speed than the flyer. (In Leonardo's device the flyer was made to rotate at the higher speed.) The difference in these speeds caused the yarn to be wound on the bobbin, while the rotation of the two elements together inserted twist into the length of yarn between the hands of the spinster and the flyer.

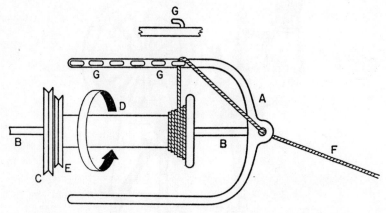

Figure 5   The flyer, spindle and bobbin of the Saxony wheel

Thus the two processes of twisting and winding were continuous, except that from time to time in Jurgens's wheel the yarn had to be transferred to another hook on the flyer leg, so as to distribute the yarn along the length of the bobbin. On the older wheel, twisting preceded winding, the whole process therefore being intermittent.

The earlier wheel is now usually referred to as the old, jersey, or muckle wheel, and the later one as the Saxony or flax wheel.

One interesting feature of Leonardo's wheel (which, incidentally, drove the spindle and bobbin through gear wheels and not by a cord) was the provision of a traversing motion which caused the bobbin to move slowly to and fro along the spindle, so distributing the thread over the entire length of the bobbin.

A development of some importance, since it was applied later to Arkwright's spinning machine, was that of dispensing with the positive driving of the bobbin from the wheel. Instead, the bobbin was pulled round by the thread as the latter rotated with the flyer, and to prevent overrunning, the bobbin was braked by means of a weighted stationary cord passing partly round a grooved flange on the bobbin. The method as applied to the wheel originated on the Continent and does not appear to have been used to any extent in Britain. An alternative arrangement, also used only in other countries, but not extensively, was that of driving the bobbin only, the flyer being pulled round by the thread.

Spinning Wheel Techniques

The techniques used when spinning on the wheels naturally varied as between the two types of wheels. They also varied even on one type, according to the kind of material being spun, and possibly also to the customs of particular districts, successive generations being taught to spin in the traditional manner in each district. Thus in the spinning of the longer kinds of wool where the fibre lengths might be anything between 10 and 16 in. (25·4 and 40·6 cm) it was sufficient, when using the Saxony wheel, to allow the 'pull' of the bobbin to draw out the strand to a finer condition, the fibre lengths being such that there was little risk of a total separation of the fibres. With the shorter wools, however, such as the wools from merino sheep, introduced from Spain about the middle of the eighteenth century, and whose fibres were only a few inches in length, it was probably often necessary to take the strain from the spinning thread, by using both hands partially to separate the fibres and then to allow some twist to 'flow' from the thread to these fibres before releasing them.

Where the material being spun on the Saxony wheel did not require the use of both hands to draw out the fibres, it was sometimes

the practice to spin two threads on the one wheel, which drove
two spindles, the spinster using one hand for each thread. Thus
efforts were made as late as 1818, though unsuccessfully, to introduce the double wheel in Ireland, because many of the flax spinsters
in Scotland used them.[3] Dyer, too, refers to the system in *The
Fleece*:

> There are to speed their labours who prefer
> Wheels double spol'd, which yield to either hand
> A several line.

The relation between stretch and twist, especially on the older
wheel, had an important influence on the regularity or evenness of
the yarns being spun. Any irregularity in thickness resulted in a
corresponding irregularity in twist distribution, the thicker places
tending to resist the flow of twist, so that as stretch was applied by
the spinster these places were more readily reduced in thickness,
whilst the thinner and more highly twisted places remained un-
drawn. This evening effect, of course, depended very much on the
skill of the spinster in determining how much stretch to apply to the
yarn in relation to the amount of twist being inserted.

Not only was it necessary to spin yarns as even and regular in
thickness and appearance as possible to ensure equally even fabric
structures, but it was also important to produce yarns of the same
thickness throughout their lengths. This thickness is expressed by
numerals which denote the 'count' of a yarn. The numerals are
based on the relation between length and mass, being expressed
either as the number of length units in a weight unit or by the
number of weight units in a length unit. In the case of cotton yarns,
the number of 'hanks' (840 yds) in 1 lb *avoirdupois* expresses the
count, e.g. a 30s yarn would measure 30 × 840 yds to 1 lb. Silk filament yarn counts or 'denier' are expressed in terms of the number
of grammes to a length of 9,000 m. Thus it will be seen that in the
cotton system the higher numbers indicate finer yarns, while in the
denier system the higher numbers indicate coarser yarns. Other
sections of the industry also have their own counting systems, but
there is little doubt that all these will be changed to one or more
systems based on metric units in the course of time.

Reverting to the need for the spinster to maintain the same thickness or count of the yarn she is spinning for, say, a particular order,

this must have been quite a difficult standard to maintain, and would depend entirely on experience in the control of the operation. That it was a real difficulty is, in fact, mentioned in Lewis Paul's patent specification for his spinning machine (Chapter 5). He states that on the wheels it was difficult 'to spin yarns of the several sorts . . . to such a degree of size or twist as may be wanted for a particular work', and adds 'weavers [were] often forced to remain unemployed for want of such particular sized yarns as are suitable to their occasions'. He goes on to claim that the use of his machine would remove this difficulty, since the drawing out was done by controlled mechanism, so that not only the yarn spun on one spindle but the yarn spun on the other spindles of his machine would all be the same count. The claim was a valid one, providing the material fed to the machine was also uniform in thickness throughout.

Further evidence of hand-spun yarn irregularities is provided by a former worsted manufacturer of Leeds, written when he was in his eighties, towards the end of the eighteenth century:

> The hand-spun yarn manufacture was an anxious and laborious occupation, requiring the eyes and hands of the master in several processes. The spinning was performed in cottage houses by the wife and children, partly in the neighbourhood and partly in the distant parts of the West Riding, in which case we employed agents, mostly shopkeepers. One obvious evil in this family work was the teaching of the children; and in sorting our yarns we not only met with whole hanks clumsily spun, but, not seldom, good and bad reeled in the same hank. This rendered the sorting of yarns a vexatious process.[4]

The techniques of wheel spinning have been described in some detail in this chapter because they are relevant to mechanical processes explained in subsequent chapters.

CHAPTER TWO

Lee's Stocking Frame

What were the motives which led the Reverend William Lee, M.A., curate of Calverton, near Nottingham, to begin making a machine which would knit stockings? One account states that it was his distress on seeing his wife incessantly hand knitting stockings to supplement his meagre income. Another story is that he paid court to a young lady who, however, instead of responding to his attentions, kept her mind on her knitting.[1] Yet another version is that the young lady employed hand knitters whose products she sold very profitably, a business which occupied all her attention to the exclusion of any thoughts of romance. So angry was the young curate at these rebuffs (in the second and third accounts) that he decided to seek a means of revenge by making a machine which in one case would deprive the lady of her hobby or in the other would take away her means of livelihood.[2] There is no evidence to show that any one of these stories is true. The overworked wife one is the least likely, since there are no records to indicate that Lee ever married. Yet there may be some truth in one of the other accounts, since he must have had some sort of incentive to cause him to begin what must have appeared to be an extremely difficult task. Failing the motives mentioned, perhaps the hand looms provided him with the inspiration—if a machine could be made to weave fabric, why not a machine to knit fabric?

The fundamental difference between knitting and weaving is that in the former it is possible, by interlooping, to use one continuous thread to form a fabric, whereas in the latter two sets of threads are interlaced. Readers will be familiar with the present-day method of hand knitting, in which plain, straight needles are used to transfer a loop from one needle to another and at the same time to interloop the thread. Fig. 6 will serve as a reminder of the method.

Certainly Lee would need to study hand-knitting techniques with

a view to mechanising the movements, and he probably also carefully analysed the structure of knitted fabrics. Yet if he watched
only the plain needles way of knitting, he would have found the
problem of converting these finger and needle movements into

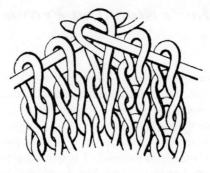

Figure 6   Hand knitting with plain needles

mechanical ones practically insoluble. It is known, however, that
many early knitting needles were hooked, and if Lee saw these in
use his problem would not be quite so difficult. The method probably led to the single-hook way of interlooping known as crocheting, and shown in Fig. 7.

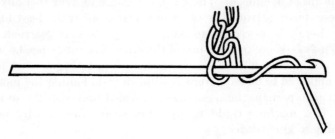

Figure 7   Crocheting

Another system of knitting at one time popular but now very
little used was that of peg knitting. There are several variations of
this form of knitting, all involving the positioning of a series of
closely set pegs round and between which a thread is passed to form a
series of kinks. The thread is then passed round and between the
pegs again, this time above the first row, and either by the fingers

or by a hook the knitter pulled the kinks of one row through the kinks of the adjacent row in the process of interlooping. Fig. 8 illustrates the process, in which the pegs carry cross-pieces C, to hold the last-formed loops. Loops 1 and 2 have been formed and the other loops in the row are the next to be lifted over the yarn Y and off the pegs.

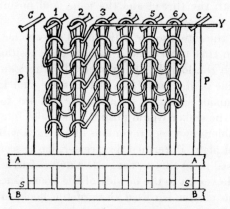

Figure 8 Peg knitting

As will be seen after a study of the knitting mechanism which Lee devised, it is feasible to assume that the inspiration for his invention came mainly from the operations involved in hand knitting with hooks, or with crocheting, although peg knitting with a hook may also have influenced him. For he decided to use the hook principle, and his efforts were directed towards providing a number of these hooks along with mechanical equivalents to hand movements, and to connect these so that they could be operated from one or more primary sources in the control of the operator. The first device with which he was able to knit had a row of twelve hooks, extending over a width of $1\frac{1}{2}$ in. $(3 \cdot 8$ cm)[3] These were fixed in a piece of wood, from which they projected horizontally. Two hooks only are shown in Fig. 9 at A, and these are spaced widely apart to simplify the drawing. A loop L of thread is shown hung from the shanks of these hooks, and a length of thread T is also laid long them. The remaining drawings in Fig. 9 are side elevations, one needle only being shown. Lee also fixed a series of metal plates, now called sinkers, in another piece of wood, so arranged that the plates were

poised in position slightly above the spaces between the needles.
These are marked S and at B are shown as having been lowered
to depress the thread T to form a series of kinks, shown in a frontal
view at the lower part of B. These kinks provide a sufficient length
of thread across the width of the row of needles for loops to be formed.
The sinkers were now made to move towards the hooks, taking
with them both the thread and the loops and pushing the thread
into the hook, as shown at C.

Comparing the action so far with that of the crocheting operation,
it will be seen that the thread T is now in a position ready to be
pulled through the loop L, or inversely, for the loop to be pushed
over the outside of the hook. It is at this stage that Lee must have
met with his major difficulty, for it is clear that any further forward
movement of the sinker would push the loop also into the hook. He
solved the problem in a very ingenious manner, as will be seen at D.
Another metal plate, P, termed the presser, has descended on to the
hook, and closed it, so that as the sinker moves further forward the
loop is pushed over on to the outside of the hook. Once this position
is reached, the presser is raised clear of the hook, and the presser
continues its forward movement until it pushes the loop off the
hook, as shown at E, resulting in the interlooping of the thread,
shown enlarged at the right of E. The sinker next moves back, taking
with it the looped threads (i.e. the knitted fabric), and another
length of the thread is laid across the shanks of the hooks. The sinker
is now ready to descend to the position shown at B for the cycle of
operations to be repeated.

The opening and closing of the hooks was undoubtedly the crux
of Lee's invention, without which the machine could not have been
operated. He made the hooks of steel, normally open, but with
sufficient spring in them to permit of their being closed by pressure.
Merely to push the hook against the shank, however, was not
satisfactory, as Lee would soon discover, for the loop tended to catch
on the point. He tried making a hole in the shank to contain this
point, but this was not successful. He next laboriously filed a groove
in the shank, so that the hook end could be well embedded in it as
shown on the right at D. This proved to be the solution of the problem, and the spring or bearded needle, as it is now called, is now in
use in thousands of knitting machines the world over.

The various movements described were made through levers and

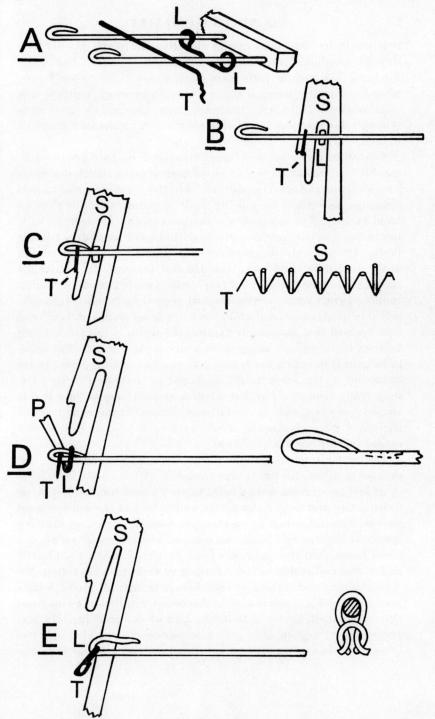

Figure 9   The knitting operation of the stocking frame

rods partly by the hands of the operator, and partly by his feet, through treadles, hence the need for him to be seated before the machine. The various parts were assembled within a wood frame, whence came the terms stocking frame, framework knitters, and frameworkers. (The word frame is now also widely used as a synonym for machine in relation to other machines in the textile industry.)

Lee, aided by his brother James, completed his machine in 1589, and his first production was a strip of narrow fabric which was made into a pair of garters. His ultimate objective, however, was to knit stockings, since these were being made in quantities at the time by hand knitters. The machine was designed to knit flat fabric, and it might be asked why he did not instead construct it to produce tubular fabric. He probably did consider this possibility, and found the mechanical difficulties too great. He had therefore to restrict his efforts to the production of flat fabric which could later be sewn into tubular form. Actually, this method proved to be one which resulted in much more satisfactory stockings being produced. For it was soon realised that by suitably varying the width of the fabric being knitted, by sometimes using more hooks (or needles, as they came to be called) to widen the fabric, and sometimes using fewer hooks to narrow it, the fabric could be shaped or 'fashioned' (hence the term 'fully fashioned') so that when sewn into tubular form it was shaped like a leg, wide at the calf and gradually narrowing towards the ankle. No such shaping would have been possible had he succeeded in knitting tubular fabric.

Lee and his brother made a few more frames, and soon Lee decided to devote his life to this work.

At first two persons were needed to work a machine, but improved construction and longer experience on the part of the knitters soon enabled one individual to operate the machine, reaching knitting speeds as high as 660 loops per minute, using worsted yarns—six times faster than the speed of a hand knitter. Lee left the Church and moved to London in order further to exploit his invention. He set up his frame in a room at his lodgings in Bunhill Fields, where his enthusiasm and pertinacity in due course resulted in a visit from Queen Elizabeth to see a demonstration of the machine. He was hoping for the grant of a patent of monopoly, but although the Queen was impressed, this was refused on the grounds that the machine would deprive thousands of hand knitters of their liveli-hood. She was also apparently disappointed to see only coarse worsted stockings where she had expected to see silk ones, and hinted that her decision might have been different had it been possible to produce the silken hose. Here, surely, was an example of one of the satirical Samuel Butler's inverted proverbs—invention indeed had become the mother of necessity.

Lee's determined character was now further demonstrated by the fact that, disappointed though he was, he set about making a frame which would knit silk stockings. No fundamental change in opera-tion was needed for this development, but as the silk yarns were much finer than the worsted yarns, it was necessary to make finer needles and to set them more closely together; in technical terms, to modify the frame so that it had a finer gauge. It was not until about 1598 that he succeeded, when naturally he presented a pair of the much-desired silk stockings to the Queen. He was again disappointed, however, for although she expressed her delight at the beauty and luxury of the stockings, no patent was forthcoming.

He continued making stocking frames, which were operated by relatives and apprentices, and after the death of Elizabeth in 1603 he had hopes of the patronage of James. He was again disappointed and was now in financial straits, having expended all he had on making the frames. It is therefore not surprising that about this time he accepted an invitation from Henry IV to visit France. He took with him his brother and 'nine workmen and as many frames'.[1] For a time all went well with him, but the assassination of the King was followed by the withdrawal of royal protection. He met with further opposition because of his Protestant faith, resulting in a complete reversal of his fortunes. He never recovered from these blows and died in poverty in France, where he was buried in 1610.[4]

Little is known of William Lee as a man. He has been described as 'having an excellent mechanical head' and as 'the first English mechanician of his own or any preceding age'. Obviously his was a forceful character, determined and persevering, while at the same time his general demeanour must have been that of a well-educated and imposing personality, enabling him to make contacts with people close to the royal court. Of his physical appearance little is known, although one not very reliable writer, with unconscious humour, refers to his 'well-knit frame'. No portrait has been preserved, although it is known that one was painted by Balderstone.

After Lee's death, his brother and a number of the others who went to France returned to England with all but one of the frames they had taken with them. These frames were installed in a building in Old Street Square, London, and formed the nucleus of the London hosiery-manufacturing industry. Later James Lee returned to Nottinghamshire, where more frames were built, and their use began to extend to other parts of the country, although London saw the greatest amount of expansion. Early in the seventeenth century the London framework knitters formed a trade association and later petitioned Cromwell to be incorporated by Charter. This was granted and subsequently granted afresh by Charles II.

The industry continued to expand. Higher knitting speeds were achieved, partly because of improved construction, partly because of the increasing skills of the workers. Other articles as well as stockings were made, including gloves, mittens, waistcoat pieces, and fabrics for other garments. Frames producing silk stockings were being worked at the rate of 1,500 loops per minute.

Although the frame was generally disliked by the hand knitters, there was little active resistance to its use at first, probably because of their lack of any organisation and because there were no special areas in which the frames were to be found in large numbers. In fact, the first machine smashings came from the framework knitters themselves, and arose from a trade recession during the reign of Queen Anne, brought about by Continental wars in which the country was involved. About one hundred frames were smashed in London and their owners, who had broken the Charter rules by employing too many apprentices, were assaulted. As a result, at least one employer moved his apprentices and machines to Nottingham, and he was later followed by others, although a colony of silk-stocking frameworkers remained in Spitalfields, amongst the silk weavers. In the 1770s, owing to the low wages being paid to these weavers, many warps on looms owned by the master weavers were destroyed by night raids on the premises, and framework knitters sometimes joined in these attacks. Later in the decade frames were smashed in Nottingham as a result of Parliament's rejection of a Bill to regulate the number of apprentices in the industry and to prevent fraudulent work being carried out.

5 Lombe's Derby silk mill 1798

6 Shuttles used before and during Kay's time

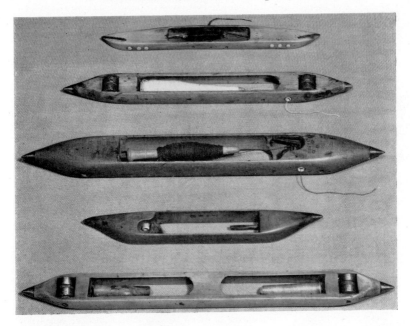

7 Jedediah Strutts

8 Spinning jenny built from Hargreaves patent specification

In spite of these interruptions and setbacks, framework knitting continued to extend throughout the Midlands. A few further improvements in detail and in the general construction of the machine were made, but substantially it remained the same in its operation until 1758—a period of 169 years from the date of its invention.

In 1730 the first pair of cotton hose was knitted on a frame in Nottingham made for knitting silk. The yarns, hand spun in India, were first made into three-, four-, or five-ply threads, and when this cotton-stocking trade began to thrive renewed attempts were made to spin suitable cotton yarns in England. Hitherto most wheel-spun cotton yarns were made for use as weft in the weaving industry. These yarns were generally required to be soft and full in texture, characteristics totally unsuitable for working on the fine needles of the stocking frame. Although nowadays Indian cotton is relatively low grade, at that time much higher qualities were being grown in some districts of India, and correspondingly fine yarns were spun. Thus all the yarns required for weaving cotton muslins were imported from India, and these were the yarns which were found suitable for frame knitting.

It was natural that efforts would now be made to spin yarns in England suitable for knitting. An interesting fact emerges from this development, namely, that the techniques of wheel spinning were very specialised—so much so that spinsters accustomed only to spinning long wools were unable to adapt themselves to the spinning of the much shorter cotton fibres, whereas those spinning short wools could do so.

The former class of spinsters resided in the Nottingham area, where they spun the long wool from Nottinghamshire sheep. The latter lived in the Tewkesbury (Gloucestershire) district and spun wool from the short Spanish merino wools used in the West of England woollen trade.

Their ability to spin cotton yarns of a thickness which needed only two-ply yarns to make them suitable for knitting (a reduction in cost of some 20 per cent) enabled the Tewkesbury framework knitters to produce much cheaper cotton stockings. The outcome of this competition was the passing of the Tewkesbury Act, 1765–6, authorising the marking of stockings other than those made of silk, to indicate the number of folds or plies in the thread used, i.e. to indicate the stronger and higher quality of the stockings made in

Nottingham. The increasing use of cotton yarns for knitting was a highly significant development in the area, and probably resulted in both Hargreaves and Arkwright, inventors of cotton-spinning machines, setting up their factories in Nottingham. This development also dispensed with the need for the Tewkesbury Act.

CHAPTER THREE

Lombe's Silk Machine

If the gossipers of Derby, during the middle years of the eighteenth century, were to be believed, the adventures of John Lombe would indeed make a story as exciting as many works of fiction, complete with a master spy, a gang of murderous and vindictive men, and a villainess to carry out their evil intentions. But many, though not all, of these stories are fictional, generated in the minds of the aforesaid gossipers and no doubt readily believed by their open-mouthed listeners.

The stories relate to the time which John Lombe is said to have spent in Italy, learning the secrets of silk processing there with a view to establishing, along with his half-brother Thomas Lombe, a silk mill in England. It was known in England in the seventeenth century that in the Piedmont district of Italy factories were operating with machinery which converted the filaments of raw silk into yarns and threads. In fact, it is believed that these processes were being carried out in the district as long ago as the thirteenth century, and that they were far more productive per operative than was possible with hand-operated spinning wheels. Certainly silk yarns were being imported into England from Italy and France in spite of prohibitive legislation in the early years of the eighteenth century, and rumours were rife that machines were being used to produce these yarns. English throwsters were deprived of work and many turned to silk weaving. The machines being used in Italy were considered to be carefully guarded secrets, yet in 1607 a book[1] was published in Padua which gave descriptions of the processes and contained illustrations showing many details of the machines. There was a copy in the Bodleian, accessible to any reader, as early as 1620, and for more than a century following, it was known to English technologists. During this period, also, the machines began to be used in France.[2]

21

It is not known whether the brothers Lombe knew of this work or of the French machines. If John did visit Italy, it might be assumed they did not know. On the other hand, even if they knew of and had access to the book, they may have found some difficulty in constructing and operating machines from drawings with descriptions in Italian and so have decided on more direct contacts. Thomas Lombe, a London merchant, was in his early thirties when it was presumably decided that John, then about twenty-three, should make the journey to Italy. He is said to have returned about the year 1717, bringing with him not only the manufacturing secrets but also some Italian workmen.

In the following year Thomas Lombe was granted a patent for 'a new invention of three sorts of engines never before made or used in Great Britaine, one to wind the finest raw silk, another to spin and the other to twist the finest Italian raw silk into organzine in great perfection, which was never before done in this country'.[3]

The doubts regarding John's visit arise from the absence of any written statement known to exist on the subject, either by Thomas or John. A year after the granting of the patent the brothers had erected a factory on an island in the River Derwent in Derby, and had begun to install machinery to be driven from a water wheel. There were probably extensions to the factory later, for there are deeds in existence which show that a lease from the Mayor and Corporation of Derby was granted to Thomas Lombe in 1724 'of two sluices at Long Byflatt and mills to be built in part of St Michaels Mills, Derby, for erecting a silk twisting manufactury.'[4]

As will be seen, the techniques required in the production of silk yarns are quite different from those used in the carding and spinning of wool or flax, which, as was described in Chapter 1, were spun on wheels from fibrous or fleecy masses of the raw materials. Silk from the silkworm *bombyx mori*, which feeds on the leaves of the mulberry tree, is extruded by the worm in a long, fine continuous filament, which it winds round itself to form a cocoon. This filament is subsequently unwound from the cocoon by operatives who wind or reel several filaments together to form a skein or hank. This operation usually takes place at or near where the silkworms have been reared and the skeins are then sent to the place, whether cottage or factory, where the actual conversion to yarn or thread takes place. It was at this stage that the factory in Derby as well as those in Piedmont began operations, and the functions of the 'three engines' mentioned in Thomas Lombe's specification may now be described. They followed the removal of gummy matter (known as sericin) on the filaments—this was carried out by immersing the skein in hot soapy water, followed by drying.

The first process was that of winding, which transferred the filaments from skein form on to small bobbins. In the second machine the strands from two or more bobbins were wound on to one bobbin, a process known as 'doubling'. The third machine twisted together the filaments on any one bobbin, and either wound each thread so produced on to a bobbin or into skein form. This is termed 'throwing'. In this process, only slight twist is inserted where the yarn is to be used as weft in weaving, but more is inserted if it is to be used for the warp. The latter yarn is the 'organzine' mentioned in the specification, the weft being usually termed 'tram'.

Because of the different method employed in twisting the silk, compared with those of the two wheels described in Chapter 1, it will be of interest to provide a brief description. Twisting on the wheels was carried out by rotating the yarn package already twisted and wound on spindle or bobbin. Silk throwing is the reverse of this action, the twist being inserted by rotating the bobbin carrying the supply of silk to be twisted. In other words, instead of winding the yarn as it is being twisted, the bobbin is unwinding. To assist in this process, a light flyer is used as a guide (a brief reference to this was made in Chapter 1). In Fig. 10 the bobbin A containing the untwisted silk is attached to and rotates with the spindle C. A second bobbin D (or, alternatively, a skein mounted on a reel) is rotated to wind the yarn, thus causing the silk on bobbin A to unwind. The flyer B, also on the spindle but free to rotate independently of the spindle, is caused to rotate as the silk unwinds, thus guiding the silk from the bobbin. So twist is inserted by the rotation of bobbin A, just as it would be if the yarn were being wound on instead of unwinding from the bobbin.

Although the above principles of throwing are the same now as they were in the Lombes' day, the 'throwing mill', as it was termed, was a vastly more complicated piece of machinery, largely owing to the clumsy construction and methods of transmitting motion. A machine of this type is shown in Plates 3 (a plan view) and 4 (an elevation). The plan view shows that the mill was circular. The

vertical axis passed down through the floor to the cog wheels connected with the water wheel. The inner circular framework was
attached to and rotated with the axis, while the outer framework,
attached to the floor, remained stationary. As the inner framework

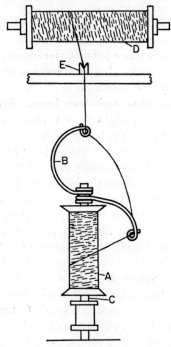

Figure 10   The flyer, spindle and bobbin of a silk throwing machine

rotated the inclined laths attached to it and shown in the sectional
elevation pushed against the pegs radiating from the drums mounted
on the outer framework, causing them to rotate. These in turn,
through gearing, turned the skeins in the lower tier and the
horizontal bobbins in the upper tier. The vertical spindles were
rotated by similar means, laths on radial arms driving pulleys on
these spindles, which, as can be seen, carried the bobbins and flyers
whose functions are described above. Such huge machines required a
correspondingly large building to contain them. 'The size of the
building suprised everyone. Five hundred feet long, five or six
storeys high, pierced by four hundred and sixty windows, it resembled a huge barracks.'[5] W. Hutton, who worked at the mill as a boy,

describes the operation of the machine:

> The work (arriving as skeins) passes through three different
> engines . . . one to wind, the second to twist, the third to double
> (to twist together two or more threads from the second machine).
> The threads are continually breaking; and to tye them is prin-
> cipally the business of children whose fingers are nimble. The
> machine continually turns a round bobbin or small block of wood,
> which draws the thread from the slip (skein) while extended on a
> swift . . . One person commands from twenty to sixty threads.
> . . . Although there are a vast number of parts, any one of which
> may be stopped and separated at pleasure; yet the whole, extending
> through five large rooms is *one* regular machine which moves and
> stops together.

It should be noted that in the machine shown in Plates 3 and 4 the
swifts drew the silk from the twisting bobbins below. Hutton was
obviously describing a winding process.

He adds that the huge water wheel made about two revolutions per
minute, and that two sluices worked four sets of mills. During the
four years in which the building was being erected Lombe hired
rooms in Derby, including some in the Town Hall, where he erected
machines which were turned by hand. The sums he received for
the silk yarns he produced on these machines paid for 'the grand
machines as the work went on'.[6]

A further description of the mill and the machines in it are to be
found in a book published in 1811: 'In the two lower rooms are the
spinning and twist mills, which are all of a circular form, and are
turned by upright shafts passing through their centres, and com-
municating with shafts from the water wheel. Their diameter is
between 12 and 13 feet; and their height 19 ft 8 in . . . each of the
four twist mills contains four rounds of spindles.'[7]

Boswell visited the mill in September 1777. Rather surprisingly,
he was not very impressed: 'I am not very conversant with mechanics; but the simplicity of this machine, and its multiple operations,
struck me with agreeable surprise.'[8] Regretably Dr Johnson did not
accompany him on this visit—it would have been interesting to have
had his comments.

The building (Plate 5) was in continuous use for the processing of
silk until 1891, when it partially collapsed and was demolished a few

years later. The original mill gates were renovated and repaired and have been re-erected on a site next to the Public Library in the Wardwick, Derby.

The silk mill was an undoubted success, and perhaps it was this success, and the death of John Lombe after a long and painful illness only three years after the erection of the mill, which originated or at least gave impetus to the stories told by the Derby gossips. As is to be expected, there are variations in the accounts which have survived, but essentially they may be condensed to the following:

John Lombe made the journey to Italy very secretly and disguised as a workman, and as such mingled with and worked amongst the silk workers in the mills there. Later he just as secretly left the country, having collected all the information he needed. The Piedmontese were so incensed when they learnt of the deception and of the success of the business in England, so the story goes, that they sent a woman to Derby to inveigle her way into his household and there to administer a slow poison to him.

There may be some little substance in the story. Thomas, in his patent application, refers to the employment of agents and to have incurred great expense and undergone hazards in order to 'discover' and to 'bring in the country' the silk machines. Again, in his application for the extension of the patent (the first case of this kind in the country), he submitted an Italian document in which it was stated that the disclosing or attempting to discover anything relating to the silk machines or their operation was prohibited on pain of death. It was again stated that Sir Thomas (as he now was) had with the greatest hazard and difficulty found out these arts and brought them to England. No details are given as to what these hazards were and, significantly, he makes no reference to his half-brother's hazards, nor to his death, which he surely would have done, had there been any truth in the poisoning story.

Although the application was rejected, an Act of Parliament was later passed granting a reward of £14,000 to Sir Thomas, one of the conditions of the award being that he should deposit models of his machine in some public institution. These were made and placed in the Tower of London, but disappeared many years ago.

The expiration of the patent rights was soon followed by installations of similar machines for throwing silk in various parts of the country, and this development is described in Chapter 17.

CHAPTER FOUR

Kay's Fly Shuttle

Weaving is a process which interlaces two sets of threads, usually at right angles to each other, the simplest form of this interlacing, 'one over and one under', or plain weave, being shown in Fig. 11, A being a view of the surface of the fabric and B a cross-section. For centuries the process was carried out on structures known as hand looms.

It is generally accepted that technical improvements in mechanisms are of a gradual nature, extending through the years and from

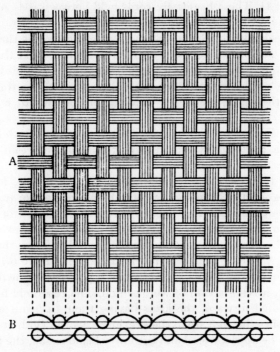

Figure 11 Interlacing of threads in plain weaving

27

generation to generation. The hand loom was no exception to this generalisation in so far as its construction and certain detailed refinements went. Yet it can hardly be true in respect of the method of passing the shuttle across the loom, an operation which was carried out for hundreds of years without any significant change.

The hand loom was and indeed is a relatively simple structure, and its operation will be easily understood by reference to Fig. 12, which is a diagram of the essential parts as they affect the yarns and their conversion into cloth. The warp yarns W have previously been wound on a roller or beam B, so that they form a sheet of closely spaced threads, their number and spacing depending upon the number of threads required in the cloth. These threads are divided at the lease rods L, so that where one thread is taken first over and then under the two rods, the adjacent ones are taken first under then over. This separation enables the weaver to locate broken threads more easily. The threads next pass through eyelets E, in the healds or heddles H. These healds are cords held between rods R. A front view of part of a 'heald shaft' is shown at Y.

Two heald shafts are shown, and some threads pass through the healds on one shaft and some through the other. Next the threads pass through the reed G, shown in a front view at Z. This is a closed comb, the 'teeth' originally made of split reeds, and the threads pass through the spaces between—usually one or two to a space or 'dent'.

One heald shaft is shown raised, the other lowered; these movements are actuated by the weaver through the treadles T and cords C.

While the warp threads are parted by this means, forming a 'shed', the shuttle S is passed by hand between them in front of the reed and supported by the sheet of lowered threads. A front view of the shuttle is shown at X. It contains the weft yarn wound on a small bobbin which rotates as the yarn is unwound, passing through an eye at F. (A similar shuttle is shown at the top of Plate 6.) This unwinding, of course, occurs as the shuttle is passed or thrown through the 'shed', leaving a trail of weft behind. The reed held by arms A is now pulled forward, the arms having their fulcrums at f. This action pushes the weft up to the previously woven cloth at J. If now the upper heald is lowered and the lower heald raised, the last 'pick' of weft will be firmly bound into position. The cycle of operations is

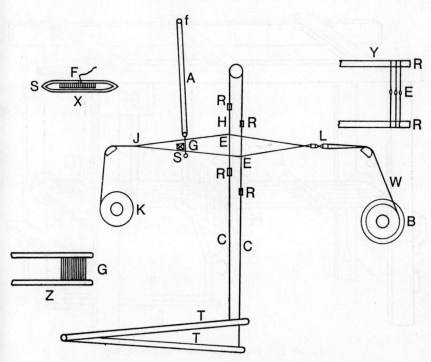

Figure 12 Diagram showing weaving actions

now repeated and from time to time the woven cloth is wound on the cloth roller K.

The perspective view of a hand loom is shown in Fig. 13, in which the features mentioned above will be recognised.

The hand loom described is of the type used before Kay's invention, and brings one back to the question posed at the beginning of the chapter—why, for centuries, did this slow and awkward method of passing the shuttle remain unchanged, having in mind the relative simplicity of Kay's method? De Gennes (see Chapter 11) in 1678 used a slow and complicated device on his loom—a pair of levers, each of which in turn took the shuttle to the middle position across the loom, whence the other then brought it to the opposite side. Vaucanson (see Chapter 11) about 1750, some seventeen years after Kay's invention, also used levers to convey the shuttle through the warp shed in his loom.

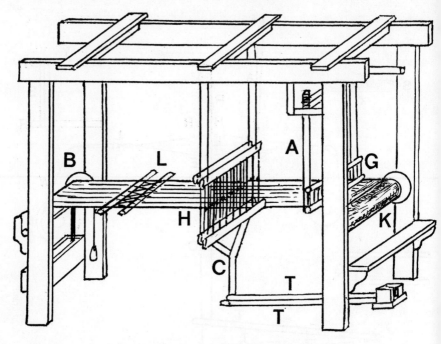

Figure 13   Perspective view of handloom

Fig. 14 shows in more detail how the shuttle was thrown or passed by hand. In wider looms two weavers were required, one seated at each side of the loom front; alternatively, one weaver would be employed, assisted by two children, who threw the shuttles across to each other. Kay's additions to the loom are shown in Fig. 15. A 'shuttle box' G was fitted to each side of the loom, connected by a long board, termed a 'shuttle race', to which the reed was attached. (It is probable that the board was used on some looms at an earlier date.) Inside each box a horizontal metal rod or spindle N was fitted, and free to slide along each rod was a 'picker' P. A cord was attached to each picker and these were joined at a stick or 'picking peg' held by the weaver as shown. By jerking the stick from side to side with the necessary force each picker in turn was caused to slide along its spindle, taking with it the shuttle and throwing the shuttle across the loom to the opposite shuttle box. Kay also fitted wheels or rollers to the shuttle to reduce the friction along the shuttle race, and these became known as 'wheel shuttles'. The second and fifth shuttles down in Plate 6 are of this type. Later the wheels were discarded and the term 'flying' or 'fly shuttle' replaced the earlier name. The operation of weaving not only became less arduous as a result of the invention but the speed could be increased. In fact, when in due

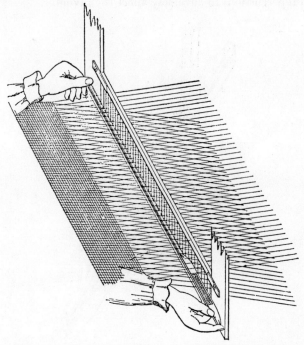

Figure 14   Handloom showing shuttle thrown by hand

course the device came into more general use, output was often doubled.[1]

John Kay was born at Park, near Bury in Lancashire, in 1704, the youngest of twelve children. His father, a yeoman farmer, died a few months before he was born. John was duly apprenticed to a reed-maker in Bury and, in a few years, had begun his own business. One of his earliest successes was that of making the reeds from metal wire instead of from split canes. These became known as 'Kay's reeds', and he was soon travelling in the surrounding country, probably by pack-horse, selling them to the master weavers—a class of weaver who also owned looms worked by others—and to the self-employed cottage weavers. The reeds were a great success, resulting in fewer yarn breakages through friction at the reed, giving increased production and better qualities of cloth. Furthermore, since unlike many later inventions, they did not create unemployment, there were no repercussions to adversely affect the inventor.

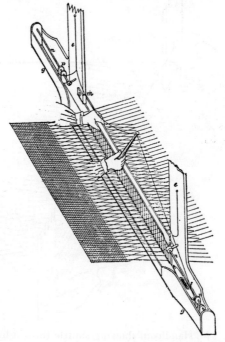

Figure 15   Handloom with Kay's fly shuttle

This could not be said of the fly shuttle, which Kay invented in 1733,[2] since, although it was slow to be adopted because of some technical difficulties and a general disbelief in its efficacy, once its advantages were demonstrated satisfactorily Kay experienced the threefold reaction common to other inventors of the times. He had the satisfaction of knowing his invention was a practical success, he suffered disappointment and shock at being maligned and persecuted by the workers, and was angered by the refusal of many weavers to pay the fifteen shillings a year which he charged for the use of his attachment. He suffered financially through lawsuit delays—many of the weavers formed 'shuttle clubs' to fight these cases.[3]

Financial difficulties resulted in his leaving the country in 1747, and settling in France, where he took out two patents, one to cover the fly-shuttle attachment, the other to cover what was known as the 'fixed bobbin'. This was a development which he had applied to his shuttle in England, but which he did not patent there. It arose out of his early difficulties in getting weavers to use his device, and in particular because, since the shuttle shot across the loom more quickly than by the hand method, so the bobbin in the shuttle rotated more rapidly to pay out the yarn. This led to more yarn breakages, and to difficulties connected with the bobbin bearings and yarn tensions. The normal manner of winding the yarn on the bobbins (they were, of course, hand wound on the wheel) was to traverse the yarn from side to side along the face of the bobbin so that parallel layers of yarn were built up. Kay's method was to wind the yarn in short traverses at one end of the bobbin to begin with, to form it so that the successive layers formed a cone, and then to continue winding on this short conical surface until the entire length of the bobbin had been filled. By this means the yarn could now be unwound over the conical end of the bobbin, and whilst the bobbin remained stationary, hence the term 'fixed bobbin'. The two forms of winding can be seen by reference to Plate 6; the top shuttle contains the older type of bobbin, and the second and third down clearly show the fixed type, with the yarn coming from the end of the bobbin and through the shuttle eye.

The change in winding technique was simple enough, and although Kay is usually credited with the innovation, he may have seen it in his travels. Certainly it overcame many of the early difficulties in operating his fly shuttle, and it is not surprising that he patented the idea in France. In that country he received official assistance and encouragement and at first things seemed to go well with him. A workshop in Paris was equipped for the manufacture of the loom parts and shuttles and at least three of his sons joined him there. But he began to meet with difficulties and became suspicious that the French officials were deliberately ignoring his patent rights. In some districts at first the loom went well; in others it failed, for reasons which are unknown.

He made several trips to England from time to time and during one of these, in 1753, a mob entered his home in Bury and smashed the furniture and the loom installed there. It is said, too, that he barely escaped with his life.[4] He later returned to France, but although the loom was by now working satisfactorily in England it was a failure in France, and Kay died there in poverty and unknown in the winter of 1780–81; it is not even known where he was interred. Later the fly-shuttle loom was again tried in France and, as in England, was so successful that it became the standard type of hand loom.

The inventive genius of John Kay has not in general been fully appreciated by historians. He had several other inventions to his credit, some of them relating to textile processes, others to other branches of engineering.[5] His fly shuttle was, of course, his outstanding achievement, which, because it increased the output of hand looms, led to an ever-increasing scarcity of yarns, and so acted as a spur to inventors intent upon the construction of machines which would spin more than one or two threads per spinster.

CHAPTER FIVE

Paul's Spinning Machine

Both Lewis Paul and John Wyatt were 'natural' inventors, and each first worked independently on ideas for converting manual operations to mechanical ones. Paul invented a machine for pinking shrouds (i.e. ornamenting them with fine perforations). It worked successfully and was a profitable venture for him. Wyatt, apprenticed to carpentering, became interested in devising a machine for boring holes in metal and another for making files, indications of his interest in mechanisms. There was another link between them— Paul was a friend of Dr Johnson, while Wyatt's family was connected with Sarah Ford, the Doctor's mother. Wyatt was born near Lichfield and was educated at Lichfield School.

Which of the two, Paul or Wyatt, first thought about a spinning machine? Opinions differ, but it is known that Paul approached Wyatt for assistance both financially and in the construction of the machine as well as to help in the experimental work. It is now generally accepted that Paul was the true inventor, but it is probable that Wyatt contributed some ideas during their experiments. There are examples of this kind of assistance by Wyatt in a letter he wrote to Paul in 1740, when they were working on a carding machine.[1] He reports on the results of various ways he was trying to remove 'ribbons' of carded material from the machine. It is not known how the idea of drawing-out by rollers was first conceived. But just as James Hargreaves (see Chapter 7) is said to have got his idea for the spinning jenny from the old spinning wheel, so it may be that roller drawing-out was developed from watching a spinster at the wheel, in this case the Saxony wheel with treadle. An explanation of the manner in which the fibres were manipulated between the fingers and thumbs of the spinster in order to prepare them for receiving the twist is given in Chapter 1, and if further consideration is now given to these actions it will be seen that there are at least

35

two possible ways in which they could be carried out by mechanisms. One would be to use two pairs of clamps or nippers, each of which could be opened and closed as well as being given movements towards and away from each other. The other and much simpler way would be to use two pairs of rollers, as shown in Fig. 16, pressures between top and bottom rollers in each pair being sufficient to hold the fibres against any pulling force, e.g. by the use of springs or weights. By turning the rollers in the directions shown by the arrows, fibres would pass from between rollers A to rollers B, and if the latter were made to rotate at a higher speed than A, and the distance from nip to nip of the rollers was made a little greater than the lengths of the fibres, the groups of fibres would be partially drawn apart, resulting in a thinner stream of fibres leaving B than was fed to A.

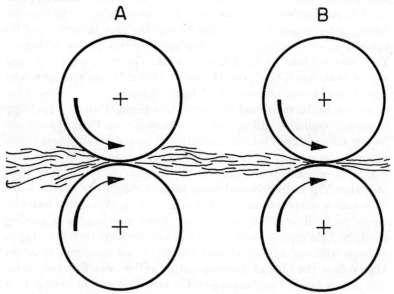

Figure 16 Drawing rollers

The roller method of drawing out was the one used by Paul and Wyatt, and later, to distinguish it from the 'stretch' spinning of Hargreaves, it was termed 'roller spinning'. As with the finger manipulations of the spinster, so here the fibres were straightened in some degree and arranged in roughly parallel formation. This drawing-out or thinning part of the process probably gave the inventors much more trouble than the subsequent twisting and winding, since they appear to have adopted the flyer and bobbin method of the Saxony wheel. In fact, the problem for the would-be inventor of a spinning machine was not concerned with these latter operations, since it was relatively easy to arrange a row or a circle of spindles and to turn them from a common source. Such machines had indeed been tried, with a child or woman seated opposite each spindle to do the spinning, obviously not a significant labour-saving arrangement. So the real problem was to multiply the actions of the spinster's hands without employing more human beings, and Paul and Wyatt probably did a considerable amount of experimenting before they began to produce results. The first patent[2] was taken out in 1738 in the name of Paul, and although there were no drawings it is clear from the wording of the specification that it covered drawing-out by pairs of rollers moving at progressively increasing speeds; but the description is complicated by references to twisting at this stage. In a second patent,[3] twenty years later, there are drawings, but they show only one pair of rollers, indicating that the slubbing was now to be 'stretched' between these rollers and the spindle, an imitation of the action in the old wheel, but since the Saxony wheel method of twisting and winding was retained, so the stretching resulted mainly from the pull exerted by the bobbin as it rotated at a higher speed than the flyer. It is possible, however, that this omission of any reference to drawing rollers may have resulted from a fear that a second patent would not be granted because of its similarity to the first, and indeed this possibility was feared at the time.[1]

The specification for the second patent shows the machine to be circular in plan like Lombe's silk mill, with a central vertical shaft to be turned by animal or water power. The 'clockwork' or gearing must have required careful construction, in relation to this circular formation, since not only the rollers but also the spindles and the bobbins were driven by this means. Parts of the circular framework rotated with the vertical axis and an upper rotating circular frame had teeth cut into its periphery which engaged with the gear wheels on short vertical shafts, and from which the rollers were driven. This method of driving was repeated around the circle—obviously continuous lengths of roller could not be used. Another circular frame below also rotated and drove by frictional contact pulleys connected with the gears for turning the spindles and the bobbins.

Fig. 17 shows a side view of the machine and Fig. 18 a similar view of a pair of rollers, a spindle, bobbin and flyer, and these do not require any further explanation.

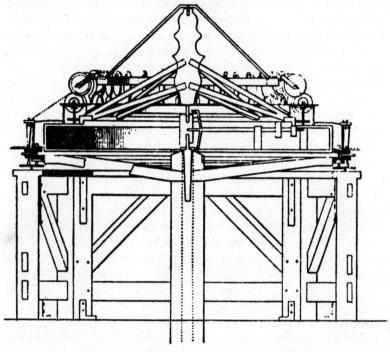

Figure 17   Paul and Wyatt's spinning machine—elevation

Reverting to the first patent, the experimental results were evidently encouraging, for about 1741 a building in Birmingham was obtained in which a machine was installed tended by ten females, the motive power being donkeys walking round a vertical shaft—the first cotton-spinning mill. The pioneers were assisted financially by some influential friends of Paul, and Dr Johnson became very interested in the scheme. A second mill was started at Northampton, in this case driven by water power, and containing five machines, each with fifty spindles. About fifty workers were employed there.

Assuming that the inventors failed to make a success of the roller-drawing principle, it is possible that later machines were constructed on the lines of the second patent, perhaps even at Northampton. To those familiar with modern roller drawing, especially of cotton, the failure is not surprising, since there are many factors concerned with the construction and adjustment of these rollers which determine their successful functioning. But it is doubtful whether cotton could be spun by the single pair of rollers method, although some classes of wool might be. So little information is available about these early machines, however, that no definite conclusions can be drawn. How successful was the machine in practice? At least one workhouse

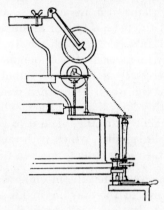

Figure 18   One pair of rollers, flyer, spindle and bobbin

was equipped with it, and Paul issued several licences to others to use the machine—150 spindles to a man in Spitalfields, 50 to a friend in Birmingham, and 250 to Doctor James, another friend, who had expressed great faith in the possibilities of the machine. There were others, too, and Paul realised several thousand pounds from these licences.[1] In all, he claimed to have made a profit of £20,000 in over twenty years (possibly an exaggeration), yet the business ultimately failed—a failure, however, which could have been due to bad management, rather than to mechanical difficulties. It is of some interest to note that at the Northampton mill Paul instituted an early example of an incentive bonus—he presented handkerchiefs to his best operators.

The greater suitability of the later machines for the spinning of

wool is shown by their use, almost up to the time of Arkwright's
spinning-machine patent, in York—there was at least one large
factory there equipped with these machines.[4] Again, there is very
little doubt that the machines referred to by the poet Dyer in *The
Fleece* were of the type invented by Paul. In fact, Dyer added a note
to his poem—'a most curious machine invented by Mr Paul'. It was
published in 1757, nineteen years after Paul's first patent and twelve
years before Arkwright's. He saw the machine either in a mill or in
a workhouse[5] situated on the banks of the Calder, near Halifax:

> A circular machine of new design
> In conic shape; it draws and spins a thread
> Without the tedious task of needless hands.
> A wheel, invisible, beneath the floor
> To every member of th' harmonious whole
> Gives necessary motion. One, intent
> O'erlooks the work. The carded wool, he says
> Is smoothly lapp'd around those cylinders
> Which, gently turning, yield it to yon cirque
> Of upright spindles, which with rapid whirl
> Spin out, in long extent, an even turne.

It is clear from this verse that the machine was constructed with
the circular plan shown in the drawing in his second patent specification. With the rollers set well back above and behind the
spindles, it would have the appearance of a huge cone, and although
the fact that the poet does not mention drawing rollers is not a
definite indication that these were not present on the machine;
when Darwin saw Arkwright's machine some years later, in his
poem, *Botanic Garden* he made special reference to the drawing
rollers in that machine (see Chapter 8).

The inventors would at an early stage in their experiments find it
necessary to provide a continuous feed of material in the form of
loose, rope-like strands ('slubbings') to the machine, and in fact the
first patent specifies this as an essential requirement. It was also
necessary for the material to be reduced to an open condition so that
the fibres were relatively free to be moved or partially separated
from each other. Paul met these requirements by constructing a
carding machine which is described in Chapter 10, and machines of
this type were installed in the two factories.

CHAPTER SIX

Strutt's Rib-knitting Attachment

The use of the stocking frame became widespread, not only in England but also in the Continental countries. In Spain the frame was largely used for the making of silk stockings, many of which were exported to England. But although increasingly used for many decades, no fundamental changes or improvements were made in the frame. There were, of course, refinements of construction, such as more accurately made needles, sinkers, and pressers, but the knitter continued to operate the various moving parts in their correct order by his hands and, through the three treadles, by his feet.

An addition to the frame was made about 1740, but it is not known who was the inventor. An Irishman is said to have introduced the device to the Nottingham knitters some time between 1740 and 1756.[1] It was and is known as a tuck presser, 'tuck' being a term used by knitters for the insertion of two or three loops on one needle. The effect of these tucks is to break up the even surface of the fabric, and if applied at the same needle or needles during every row or 'course' across the fabric, the result is a distinctive line or rib running down the length of the hose. If the tucking is applied at adjacent needles, say alternatively, a zigzag line is produced.

To form these tuck stitches, a second presser was required. This was a thin metal bar arranged above the usual pressers and grooved at its lower edge. As this presser descended it closed the needle springs or beards, so allowing the yarn loops to pass over them. Where there was a groove in the presser, however, this allowed the corresponding needle to remain open until pressed by the usual presser. It was also possible to move the metal strip sideways to produce the zigzag effect mentioned.

The tuck presser was not a development of outstanding importance. Nevertheless it was something new and may have set knitters

41

thinking about other possible improvements and developments. The
greatest need at the time was a means for enabling the frameworker
to produce ribbed stockings. Readers will be familiar with the rib
knit, to be found in hose, and in the cuffs and collars of knitted outer-
wear and underwear. It provides a much more elastic structure,
which fits more closely than a plain knitted one, yet is easily
stretched.

Hand knitters know that the rib is produced by reversing the
loops in straight lines down the hose, and this was the problem to be
solved—how to turn about or reverse the loops by mechanical means.
So great was the need for these ribs that sometimes machine-knitted
hose was taken from the frame and ribbed by hand. To do this
'runs' were allowed to form in the hose at suitable intervals, and the
yarn was then relooped the reverse way by a hand-manipulated
hook.

Several attempts were made by would-be inventors to devise a
method of reversing the loops by mechanism during the knitting
process, and there was much discussion amongst the framework
knitters, hosiers, and others on the subject. Amongst these was a
hosier, i.e. an employer of frame knitters, William Woollet, of
Derby, who discussed the matter with his brother-in-law, Jedediah
Strutt, a farmer of Blackwell in Derbyshire. But Strutt was more
than a farmer, he was a man with a flair for mechanical invention.
As a boy he had made small water wheels which he operated in a
near-by stream. Later he made an improved plough, and experimented with wheels and levers as part of his studies in mechanics.
It was no doubt Woollet's knowledge of these interests of his brother-
in-law which led him to mention the need for a rib-forming mechanism, even though at the time Strutt had no knowledge of the
stocking frame.

Nevertheless he became interested and began studying Lee's invention in detail, and to consider how the loops might be reversed
during the knitting process. He found the problem extremely
difficult to solve. Here was no sudden inspiration but instead prolonged and expensive experimental work. He finally succeeded and
patents were taken out in 1758[2] and 1759.[3] The result was not a
separate machine, nor was it an improvement in the usual sense on
Lee's frame. It was an addition or attachment which, to quote one
of the specifications, was 'furnished with a set of turning needles

and to be fixed to a stocking frame'. These needles were set in a near-vertical position and spaced between the horizontal needles in Lee's frame. In operation, after each looping action made by the usual needles, the rib-forming needles moved between them and entered the last-formed loops, which passed under the bearded hooks of the ribbing needles. During this action the loops were reversed, so producing the ribbing effect.

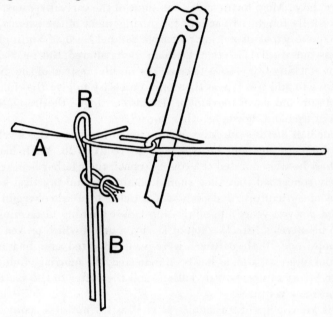

Figure 19 Strutts rib-forming attachment

Fig. 19 will serve to illustrate a very simplified description of the action. The rib-forming needle R (there is, of course, a row of these corresponding to the spaces between the knitting needles) has moved away from the knitting needles (see Fig. 9, Chapter 2) and the presser A has closed the beard. The plate B moves upwards, pushing or 'knocking over' the previously formed loop and so adding another loop to the fabric. The needle R next moves towards the sinkers S, the plate B descends and the next cycle of knitting operations begins with the rib-forming needles operating from the opposite side.

The principle underlying the operation of the attachment is still that of today's mechanisms, and became the basis for many later developments. Improvements have, of course, been made, including modifications to accommodate the actions to the power-driven machines which were evolved later. The device proved to be a great success, and Strutt left his farm to set up business in Derby along with Woollet to manufacture what soon became known as Derby-ribbed hose. More fortunately than some of the early inventors, they successfully fought two actions for infringement of the patents, and subsequently took in another partner—Samuel Need, of Nottingham. It was not until 1777 that William Betts altered the mechanism in the stocking frame so as to cause the needles instead of the sinkers to move to and fro. It was then only necessary to give the sinkers a simple up and down movement. He also arranged the frame 'to be worked by hand, horse, or other power'.[4]

Jedediah Strutt's ancestors had occupied land near Blackwell for many generations and he was born there in 1726. With his two brothers he was educated at a county school, their father being particularly concerned that they should obtain a sound practical knowledge of agriculture. Jedediah was articled to a wheelwright and served a seven years' apprenticeship before turning to farming. In 1755 he married Miss Woollet of Derby, a union which proved to be a happy one. Both partners were well educated and had many mutual interests, and, as has been indicated, the marriage indirectly led to Strutt's important inventions and thereafter to the success of his business ventures.

His knowledge of mechanics as well as his business acumen led him later to encourage and indeed to enter into partnership with Arkwright in the latter's development of his spinning machine, an occurrence more fully described in Chapter 8. Although the partnership was dissolved after a few years, Strutt went on to develop his businesses in both hosiery manufacture and cotton spinning, and these were continued successfully by later generations.

CHAPTER SEVEN

Hargreaves' Spinning Jenny

It has often been stated that James Hargreaves got his idea for a spinning machine from seeing an overturned jersey-spinning wheel. Although these stories have no foundation in fact, it is possible that this did happen.[1] For the first spinning jenny was little more than the jersey wheel laid on its side, with several vertically positioned spindles being turned from the large wheel. There was one addition—a length of wood split in two and used as a clasp to hold several slubbings in place of the single slubbing held in the spinster's hand. Here, in fact, was another answer to the problem discussed in Chapter 5—that of finding a way of duplicating the spinster's hands.

This first spinning jenny may have been made about 1764, possibly a year or two earlier.[2] About this time the hand-loom weavers were experiencing great difficulty in obtaining sufficient yarns for their requirements, mainly because they were now using Kay's fly-shuttle attachment and consequently producing more cloth. The patent rights had long since expired and early prejudices and difficulties had been overcome. The yarn shortage had resulted in the Society of Arts, in 1761, offering rewards for the invention of a machine which would 'spin six threads of wool, flax, hemp or cotton at one time, and that will require but one person to work and attend it.' A number of machines were submitted to the Society during the next few years, but none was considered worthy of the rewards. Hargreaves did not submit his invention—he may not have known of the offer, or he may have preferred to keep his machine secret. Certainly as a hand loom weaver himself he would know of the yarn shortage and this fact alone could have led him to think about a spinning machine.

He had earlier given indications of having an inventive mind as well as skills as a carpenter and mechanic. He had devised improved methods of carding and had constructed 'stock cards' (carding sur-

45

faces fixed on benches, over which hand cards were passed in the carding process, for use in the cottages in the district). These achievements had led Robert Peel, a neighbouring farmer who had become interested in calico printing as well as in manufacturing, to ask him to assist in the making of a carding machine (see Chapter 10). Later the two became closely associated in the development of the jenny, whose potentialities Peel had quickly recognised. Robert Peel was the father of the first baronet, Sir Robert Peel, whose son became Prime Minister of Great Britain. The family had an important influence on the early developments in the textile industry, establishing factories in various districts of Lancashire.

At an early stage in his experiments Hargreaves no doubt realised that there was a limit to the length of his clasp beyond which it became too unwieldy to handle without other support, and a natural step would be to build a framework on which the clasp could be placed and moved about. This he did, and Fig. 20 shows in diagram

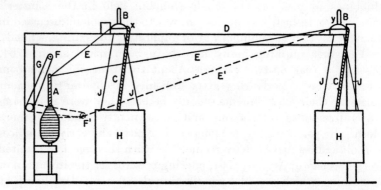

Figure 20   Diagram of the spinning jenny

how the arrangement probably operated—the wheel and driving of the spindles being omitted for simplification. The drawing shows the clasp B, known also as the clove (in Yorkshire), the drawbar and the slide, resting on the frame D. The clasp is shown in two positions, on the left at the beginning of the drawing out operation, and on the right at the completion of the drawing out. The spinner stood on the right of the clasp, and as he drew it along with one hand he opened and closed the clasp to release and to hold the slubbings drawn from the box H in imitation of the actions of the spinster's hands. At the same time he turned the wheel with his free hand, so driving the spindles A and twisting the thread or yarn E. At the end of the outward movement of the clasp the surplus coils on each spindle had to be removed and the spun length wound on the 'cop'. Instead of imitating the spinster's action, however, which would require the clasp to be moved through a different plane towards the spindles, Hargreaves fitted a wire F on levers G, controlled through a wire connection by the operator, so that as he or she reversed the spindles wire F was moved downwards to take up the slack yarn, as shown by the broken lines. The spindles were now turned in their original direction, the closed clasp pushed towards the spindles and the wire F moved up and down to guide the yarn on to the cop. Obviously, the technique of evening out the slubbings by twist-stretch controls (see Chapter I), also applied to the jenny.

Some instructions found in a notebook at the Bean Ing Mill, near Leeds, for spinning woollen yarns on the jenny, are of interest.[3] They relate to the early years of the nineteenth century, and include the following: 'Put the clock back, draw the slide sharply over the threads, lock up quick, untwine the sloobing and draw carefully out, when you put up let the slide move quickly over the threads or else the sloobing will twist, these things are best learnt by watching the men. The clock is for telling what thickness you are spinning.'

The clock referred to was a recording device fitted to the framing at one side and having a projecting lever which was struck by the slide at each outward movement. A dial with two indicators showed the number of 'draws' made, and the reference to yarn thickness was no doubt related to the number of draws and therefore the total length of yarn wound on a cop. By weighing the completed cop the weight per unit of length or the length per unit of weight could be ascertained, thus giving an indication of the thickness of the yarn. It will be seen, too, that much importance was attached in the above instructions to the prevention of too much twist passing through the open slide—such an occurrence would make the drawing out more difficult, if not impossible.

A few years ago, T.M.M. (Research) Ltd, Helmshore, Lancashire, the research department of Textile Machinery Makers Ltd, at the suggestion of Mr C. Aspin, of the Helmshore Local History Society, constructed a spinning jenny from Hargreaves's patent specification, and two views of this are shown in Plate 8. The slubbings are shown as having been wound on tubes or spindles—the old wheel would be used for this purpose. They pass under and then between the clasp, emerging to be drawn out between clasp and spindles. The spindles were turned through strings or bands from the near-horizontal wheel, fitted with a handle, each spindle having its own driving band. A full account of this interesting experiment has been published,[4] along with other information about Hargreaves and his achievements. Since the patent specification was not published until six or more years after the first jenny was constructed, it would include improvements made as a result of experience with older machines, and the experimental machine would not therefore represent the earliest examples.

Important later improvements made by other inventors included that of placing the wheel in a vertical position, which made it more accessible to the spinner, and devising a drive from the wheel to a cylinder which extended along the length of the machine. Bands from this cylinder then drove the spindles. In another improvement the drawbar was mounted on wheels.[5] These are shown in Fig. 21, and Plate 9, the latter also showing the clock, which can be seen in front of the wheel. The improvements made it much easier for the machine to be worked, and so longer machines began to be constructed, which, of course, had to be installed in sheds and were worked by men. But jenny spinning also continued as a cottage industry, the smaller machines being worked by women and children.

James Hargreaves was probably born about 1719–20 in the district of Oswaldtwistle, between Accrington and Blackburn, and it was after his marriage and while living in a cottage (which is still to be seen there) in the near-by hamlet of Stanhill that he invented the jenny. He probably worked on it in secret for some time, since Robert Peel is said to have become inquisitive when he discovered that more than the usual quantities of cotton weft were being produced in the district. When he taxed Hargreaves with being responsible, Hargreaves showed him the machine and, in due course, he made some for installation in Peel's mill; he also made some for his (Hargreaves') relations and friends.

The new 'engine' began to be talked about in the neighbourhood and fears began to be expressed regarding its possible effects on the livelihood of the cottagers. About the year 1768 there were attacks on Hargreaves' home, during which his furniture was destroyed and all the windows smashed. The framework of some twenty jennies stored in a near-by barn was also destroyed along with all the working implements.[6] (When, a few years later, machine breaking again broke out, the smaller jennies, such as were used in the homes, were spared.)

Figure 21 Improved spinning jenny

During the 1768 rioting Hargreaves remained in hiding and at the earliest opportunity left the district for Nottingham. In the circumstances, it seemed at the time a very appropriate centre in which to make a new start with the jenny. The demand for cotton yarns for use in the stocking frame was growing, and it may be that some interested person there invited Hargreaves; alternatively, he may have known of the situation, possibly through Peel or the partners in his business. Hargreaves secretly constructed some jennies for a man named Shipley and shortly afterwards entered into partnership with Thomas James, also of Nottingham. Together they built a mill and ran, for some years, a relatively successful cotton-spinning business.[7]

It was not until the business had been established that Hargreaves, in 1770, applied for a patent for the jenny. It is not known why he waited so long before seeking this protection. Ignorance of procedure or even lack of finance should not have prevented him, since he would have had the advice and support of Peel. Had he taken out a patent at first the whole course of his life might have been changed. Even in Nottingham he seems to have applied for a patent on the advice of James, although the fact that Arkwright (see Chapter 8) had patented his spinning machine the year before may also have influenced him. It was, in fact, in the interests of both partners to try to protect themselves in this way, since not only in Nottingham[8] but also in Lancashire rivals were building jennies and working them. In June of that year they advertised that they would take legal proceedings against infringers of the patent, but this and other efforts to protect themselves were finally rendered ineffective by the disclosure that Hargreaves, while in Lancashire, had sold some jennies to buy clothing for his children, and could not therefore claim patent protection with any hope of success.

In spite of this blow, the partners continued the business with relative success for a year or two, and it is somewhat ironic to consider that had the mill been situated in Lancashire instead of in Nottingham it would have prospered for a much longer period. The reason for this was that Arkwright, too, had established a mill in Nottingham and was spinning cotton yarns there on his machines. By 1722 he was employing three times more labour in this mill than were Hargreaves and James in theirs, and the yarns he was producing were found to be much more suitable for knitting than were the jenny-spun yarns. It is not surprising, therefore, to find that the demand for the latter began to decline and that by about 1776 Hargreaves and James discarded their jennies and installed Arkwright's machines under licence.

Yet in Lancashire the jennies were becoming more and more popular. This popularity was mainly due to the fact that jenny-spun cotton yarns, though totally unsuitable for use on the fine, delicate needles of the stocking frame, possessed the right characteristics for weft yarns in the cotton-linen fabrics being produced in large quantities at the time by hand-loom weavers. Subsequently, when these fabrics were replaced by all-cotton goods, the weft continued to be jenny-spun. In the woollen industry, also, the jenny was found to be an efficient machine for spinning the soft full yarns required. Another factor which influenced the popularity of the jenny was its

9 Improved spinning jenny showing the 'clock'

10 A water frame from Cromford Mill

11 Sir Richard Arkwright

12 Lapping machine used in Arkwright's Mills

simple construction and relative cheapness, so that not only the cottagers but the small manufacturer of limited resources was able to purchase the machine.

Having regard to this extensive and prolonged use of the jenny, it is evident that James Hargreaves has been very much underrated as an inventor. The importance of his invention is generally considered very secondary to that of others of his day, yet, apart from the widespread use of the jenny, it should also be remembered that part of Crompton's invention of the mule was inspired by the spinning jenny.

Although there is little doubt that Hargreaves did invent the jenny, one claimant to the invention put forward the argument that he named his machine the jenny after one of his daughters. (Neither Hargreaves's wife nor either of his daughters bore this name.) The claimant was Thomas Highs, who stated that he had earlier invented a spinning machine similar to that of Hargreaves. An illustration purporting to be Highs's 'jenny', however, shows a very different construction, with the drawbar moving in a vertical direction—an action which would have been difficult to operate.

Regarding the derivation of the word jenny, it is generally accepted that this stems from the word engine—a term commonly used at the time for any kind of machine. Hargreaves even uses the word in his patent specification to describe his machine, and until quite recently textile machinery makers' catalogues usually referred to 'carding engines'. In some districts of Yorkshire the horse-driven axis used for driving the early machines was termed a 'horse-gin'. So 'gin', 'ginny', 'jinny', and 'jenny' were contractions of 'engine'. Nevertheless, Highs had abilities as an inventor, his name being usually associated with the Arkwright Case, when he claimed to have invented Arkwright's spinning machine (see Chapter 8). He exhibited a double-sided jenny, i.e. a machine in which the large driving wheel was in the centre instead of at the side, in the Manchester Exchange in 1772. It was an innovation which was later applied to the mule by others.

James Hargreaves died and was buried in Nottingham in 1778, practically unknown, for there were no public references to his death at the time. He did not die in poverty, however. He and his partner James had continued to be actively engaged in spinning cotton yarns, and Hargreaves's widow received the value of her husband's share of the business, along with property bequeathed to her by her husband.

Before considering the subsequent inventions of Arkwright and Crompton, it will be of some interest to examine briefly another spinning machine which, although not successful, was an attempt to combine the stretching actions of the jenny with the bobbin and flyer system of spinning. The inventor was Coniah Wood, and the machine was patented in 1772.[9] Fig. 22 is a side elevation of part of the machine, based on a drawing in the specification, but omitting most of the framework. The fibres to be spun (wool and flax are

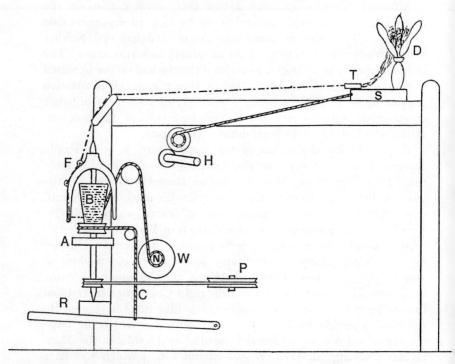

Figure 22   Coniah Wood's spinning machine

mentioned) were withdrawn from a distaff or rock D and taken through a compressing tube T to the flyer F. The sliding board S, to which the distaff and tube were attached, was moved away from the flyers by turning the handle H, drawing out the material as the flyer and bobbin, driven from the pulley P, revolved as one unit. So far the principle is similar to that of the jenny, providing a stretching action during twisting. To wind the spun yarn on to the bobbin B, the board S is moved towards the flyers, and the treadle R is depressed to apply a brake on the bobbin through the cord C, so that the rotating flyer now winds the yarn on the stationary bobbin. It will be seen that there is only one hook on the flyer leg to act as a yarn guide to the bobbin. This was possible because the bobbin was given an up-and-down movement through the rail A by turning the wheel W on the shaft N, causing the yarn to be wound along the length of the bobbin. The drawing in the specification shows four of these bobbins and flyers in a row, with a corresponding number of distaffs and tubes, all controlled through the wheels and levers indicated.

CHAPTER EIGHT

Arkwright's Spinning Machine

There are differences of opinion regarding the inventive abilities of Richard Arkwright. Some authorities believe that the roller spinning frame at least was largely based on his own ideas and experiments, while others are of the opinion that in every development of machinery in which he engaged he used the ideas and inventions of others. All agree, however, that he readily saw the potentialities of machinery inventions, and that he possessed the perseverance, determination, and drive to turn these into practical and commercial successes.

Of all the early inventors, he was the one who started life under the heaviest handicaps and who in the end gained the greatest financial success. He was born in Preston, Lancashire, in 1732, of poor parents, and one of thirteen children. He had little or no schooling, although he succeeded in learning to read and write, perhaps an early indication of his persevering nature. Apprenticed to a barber, he subsequently set up in business for himself as barber and wig-maker in Bolton, and some years later began travelling the country, buying human hair for his wig-making business. An early example of his business instincts was shown by his obtaining or possibly inventing a formula for dyeing hair, a development which enabled him to sell dyed hair to other wig-makers.

The decline in the demand for wigs, due to a change in fashion, caused Arkwright to seek other means of livelihood. Like Hargreaves, he would know that there was a general shortage of yarns for weavers because of Kay's invention—in fact, owing to his contacts with many people as he travelled about the country, he probably heard much more about the scarcity, and this may have set him thinking about a spinning machine. But there was another factor which possibly had a greater influence in this direction. In 1761 he had married Margaret Biggins of Leigh, in Lancashire, his first

56   THE TEXTILE INDUSTRY

wife having died. He probably knew the town well, and would have
heard of a reed-maker and mechanic there who was experimenting
with machine models and who was employing a clockmaker named
John Kay (in no way associated with the inventor of the fly-shuttle
attachment) to help him in his work. The inventor was Thomas
Highs, already mentioned as a claimant to the invention of the
jenny. Highs claims that at this time he was working on a roller
spinning machine and that Kay was making a model for him. What is
certain is that Arkwright induced Kay to work with him and that
together they began experimenting with a roller spinning machine
for cotton. In 1768 they took the model to Preston and worked on it
in a room in the Free Grammar School there.[1] Whether Highs or
Arkwright is to be considered the 'inventor' of the machine, the fact
remains that Paul and Wyatt had invented a similar machine thirty
years earlier, though neither Highs nor Arkwright would admit any
knowledge of it. The drawing rollers, spindles, flyers, and bobbins,
all the parts essential to the actual processing of the cotton, functioned in the same manner. Only the driving connections were
different—instead of a machine circular in plan and working from a
vertical central axis, they devised one which was rectangular. This
arrangement was much simpler to construct and to operate, as can
be seen by reference to Fig. 23 taken from the patent specification.[2]
A model of the machine may be seen in the Science Museum,
London.

If Paul and Wyatt's machine is recalled, there will be no difficulty
in understanding Arkwright's. The drawing rollers are shown at I,
the slubbing bobbins being behind these. The yarns emerging from
the rollers are marked M, and pass down to the flyers Q and
bobbins P. One important difference between this machine and Paul
and Wyatt's was that whereas the bobbins in the earlier machine
were directly driven, following the principle of the ordinary Saxony
wheel, in which the bobbin was turned by a driving band, Arkwright
adopted the method used in some parts of the Continent, where the
bobbin, suitably braked, was pulled round by the yarn (Chapter 1).
At first he used hooks on the flyer legs, as in the Saxony wheel, an
arrangement which necessitated frequent stoppages of the machine
to rethread the yarn.

The simplicity of the driving mechanism for the machine is
obvious—a vertical shaft at the side, projecting through the floor and

driven below by animal or water power, was fitted with a large
pulley B from which a belt C drove a row of spindles. Another
vertical shaft G also driven from the belt drove the toothed wheel H
and the 'clockwork' gearing behind it which turned the rollers. A

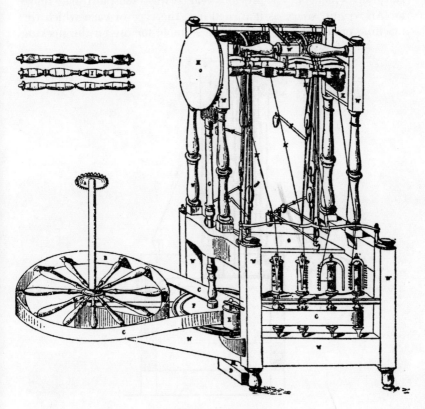

Figure 23 Arkwright's roller spinning machine

side sectional view of the machine is shown in Fig. 24. Four pairs of
drawing rollers are shown with a system of lever weighting, but the
hooked flyers are still retained.

The cost of the experiments reduced Arkwright and his family to
a condition of extreme poverty, but some success must have resulted,
since he persuaded a Preston publican and paint merchant named

Smalley to become his partner and so provide further finances. But rumours of a new machine which would take away the livelihood of the people in the district brought hostility and threats, and the experimenters decided to take the machine to Nottingham, where Hargreaves had gone the previous year. It was a most fortunate move for Arkwright, since, as it turned out, the type of yarn which the machine produced was much more suitable for use on the stocking

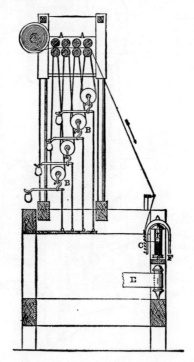

Figure 24   Arkwright's roller spinning machine, side section

frame there than were the jenny-spun yarns. More fortunate still, Arkwright found a partner who not only understood and helped him in improving his machine but also provided the capital he so urgently needed. This was Jedediah Strutt, now well established as a successful hosiery manufacturer and as such interested in any development which would supply him with cotton yarns for his stocking frames. Another hosiery manufacturer who joined them in the venture was

Samuel Need of Derby. Smalley, on the other hand, seems to have ceased being a partner at this stage, but was retained as a manager.

Together they established a small mill in Nottingham, where Arkwright, Smalley, and Kay installed a number of spinning machines which were driven by horse power. Arkwright now took out his patent for the machine. Some of his detractors have stated that in this patent he described himself as a 'clockmaker', and that this falsehood provided further evidence of his wrongful claims to the invention. Actually there is no reference to Arkwright's occupation, and it is difficult to understand why his enemies used such an argument, since it could so easily be refuted. (Others, indeed, have asked why Highs later allowed twenty years to elapse before publicly claiming to be the inventor.)

Even under the crude and primitive conditions prevailing in this small mill, the yarns produced must have proved reasonably satisfactory for the hosiery industry, for in 1771 a larger mill, driven by water power, was erected on the banks of the River Derwent at Cromford, in Derbyshire. Because of this source of power, Arkwright's machine soon became known as the water frame, and the machine shown in Plate 10 was originally used in the Cromford mill. It is a double-sided machine, having twenty-four spindles on each side. There are three pairs of drawing rollers, the upper one covered with leather to provide a cushion-like surface by means of which considerable pressure could be applied between the rollers so as to grip the cotton without injuring the fibres. The cushioning was particularly necessary because of the very heavy weighting applied to the top rollers at the time (some of the weights may be seen on the floor in the illustration), certainly much heavier than was later found necessary. Possibly the crude construction of the rollers and their bearings, and the general unevenness of the roller surfaces made the heavy weighting necessary.

The frame was driven from a vertical shaft (shown on the extreme left) which was driven from the water wheel through gearing in the room below. Actually two machines were driven directly from the same shaft, the second machine being in the same line and further to the left. A large wood bevel wheel at the upper end of the vertical shaft originally drove a square-section wood shaft which extended across the room to drive other machines. Fig. 25 is a drawing of the front elevation of a similar machine. A lever E, D with connections is shown which operated a clutch to start or stop each machine. A similar clutch may be seen in the photograph.

It can be seen also that the flyers are no longer hooked. This was because mechanism had now been added to the machine which traversed the bobbins slowly up and down within the arms of the flyers, so distributing the yarn along the lengths of the bobbins. (The first patented traversing device appears to have been that of Coniah Wood, in 1772, which is described in Chapter 7. It was hand operated, and it is unlikely that Arkwright's motion was based on this.)

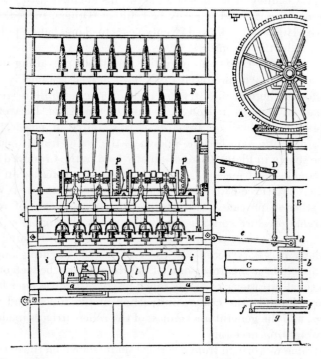

Figure 25 Improved water frame, front elevation

Soon after the erection of the Cromford mill a second mill was built at Belper, a few miles away, and also driven by water power. It was of the spinning machines at these mills that Erasmus Darwin wrote in his *Botanic Garden*, in which he specifically describes the drawing rollers:

> With quickened pace successive rollers move
> And these retain and these extend the rove;
> Then fly the spokes, the rapid axles glow,
> While slowly circumvolves the labouring wheel below.

It was at these mills that the factory system, as it is known today, began and was developed. It is described in Chapter 14, but to appreciate what this organising involved, some knowledge of the processing machines which were devised and put into operation at the mills is necessary. The machine carding of the cotton (see Chapter 10) was probably the first step towards further mechanisation to prepare the material for the spinning machine. Both Paul and Hargreaves, it will be recalled, adopted the same procedure.

But these two types of machines were not enough. There were two very different problems to face if more mechanisation was to be introduced. One was the picking and cleaning of the raw cotton, a slow, laborious operation carried out by women and children, and relatively costly in labour charges. The other was the need for better preparation of the material after carding and before it reached the spinning machine.

Opening and Cleaning the Cotton

Much of the cotton imported during the eighteenth century probably contained the seeds as well.[3] In fact, the whole cotton boll or pod seems to have been included, if the following extract, again from the *Botanic Garden*, is to be relied upon:

> First, with nice eye, emerging naiads cull
> From leathery pods the vegetable wool.

Darwin's poetic fancy also surrounds the women and children in a 'sea' of raw cotton.

Severe beating of the cotton in an attempt to remove the pods and seeds would only break them into smaller pieces, making extraction more difficult. The fibres were probably pulled from the seeds by hand, but 'bowing' sometimes followed this picking in order to loosen and release broken leaf and other impurities. It was a process in which the strings of bows were embedded in the cotton and plucked; the resulting vibration then loosened the cotton. An early machine for opening and cleaning cotton consisted of a rotating cylindrical cage made of interwoven willow canes. The cotton was placed in the cage and the agitation it received within the cage loosened it and allowed impurities to fall from the cage. Another hand method consisted of spreading the cotton on a net and 'batting' or beating it gently with canes. John Kay, the inventor of the fly-shuttle attachment, patented a machine which imitated this action, but he appears to have intended it for wool. Similar machines, however, were later used in cotton mills—they were known as 'batting machines' and it is probable that much of the cotton was by this time being more effectively 'ginned', i.e. freed from seeds (see Chapter 14).

A development of the rotating cage was also probably brought into use as more seedless cotton began to arrive at the mills. In this case a cylinder with projecting spikes rotated inside a stationary cylindrical cage and the cotton was struck by these spikes and flung against the cage. More drastic treatment of the cotton resulted from the use of two spiked cylinders in juxtaposition, which between them tore the masses of cotton into smaller pieces.[4] Both types of machines were known as 'devils'—in fact, this term seems to have been used for several kinds of opening machines in different sections of the textile industry—and it is probable that the rougher treatment of the cotton became more necessary as the bales from the cotton-growing countries became more densely pressed.

Arkwright doubtless used one or more of the opening machines described above. Certainly other cotton-spinning mills had them and these may have been copies of those used by Arkwright just as he used machines originated by others. There is evidence, too, that some of these early attempts in the mechanical opening of cotton resulted in the production of inferior-quality yarns, probably due to the fibres being damaged.

The use of spiked cylinders was in due course developed and larger and faster moving cylinders and cones became the generally accepted means for opening and cleaning cotton, these being enclosed and either completely or partly surrounded by gridded surfaces. Also, instead of having to stop the machines at intervals to remove the opened cotton and to insert more cotton, the process became continuous by the provision of feed aprons, feed rollers, and delivery apertures.

A method of delivering the opened cotton which came to be

generally adopted may have first been devised by Snodgrass in 1787, and used at Johnstone near Paisley in Scotland. The machine was termed a scutcher, no doubt because a beater was used which struck the cotton much in the same way that flax was 'scutched' (see Chapter 19). The beater consisted of a central shaft from which projected radial arms carrying bars—usually two—which struck the cotton as it was fed into the machine.

The machine was described as a 'scutching or blowing machine', which implies also that the cotton was blown through the machine, perhaps because the beater also acted as a fan. This air movement could therefore drive the opened cotton out of the machine at some delivery point. There is no doubt that Arkwright used a machine of this type and indeed made improvements on it. It is mentioned by G. B. Strutt, a son of Jedediah Strutt, in the evidence he gave before the Select Committee on Children in Manufacture in 1816, when he read Arkwright's own description:

> The scutching machine most in use is a machine for cleaning cotton from the seeds and other impurities and is in principle similar to the threshing machine. The cotton passes through a pair of rollers and is struck by bars of iron or steel called beaters which revolve with great velocity striking the cotton with considerable force over a number of parallel bars so placed as to allow the seeds to fall through.

He goes on to describe how the cotton is further cleansed, and this part of the process appears to have been an extension developed by Arkwright and his associates. He refers to the cotton being taken by a current of air 'into an apartment called the cotton chamber'. A rotating fan inside the chamber drew the air and dust through a 'fine wire grating' whilst preventing the cotton from passing through. In this way the cotton was further cleansed and the dust which would otherwise have been released from the cotton at later stages to contaminate the atmosphere, was taken by 'a chimney or funnel to the outside of the building'.

A somewhat detailed account has been given of the scutcher and of the use of air currents, because they were the beginning of methods of opening and cleaning cotton which were later to be extensively developed. Air currents in particular generated by fans within the machines have since played an important part in the conveying and cleaning processes, and just as the 'bell-tower' was a common adjunct in the roof of the early cotton mills, so the square-topped tower which allows air currents generated in the 'blowing-room' (where the opening machines and scutchers are situated) to pass into the open is a feature of later buildings. The dust and other fine impurities remain in the dust-settling chamber below.

At first, the opened and cleaned cotton was taken in bulk and spread by hand to the carding machines (see Chapter 10), but before the end of the eighteenth century a simple 'lapping machine' was devised, consisting of a long feed apron on which the cotton was spread, rollers which compressed the sheet of cotton, and a device which rolled the sheet to form a 'lap' round a central roller or rod. In this form the material could be conveniently taken to the carding machine where the lap unrolled as the sheet entered the machine. Plate 12 shows a lapping machine which was used in one of Ark-wright's mills. Later lapping mechanism was incorporated with the scutcher, and a machine of this type is shown in Fig. 26, where B is the beater, C the parallel bars or grid, and G a delivery apron which conveyed the cotton to the lapping mechanism on the left.

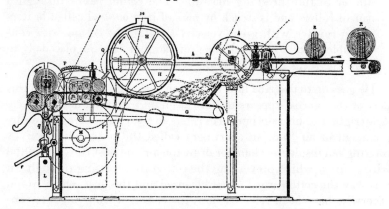

Figure 26 Early scutcher, sectional elevation

More Preparation for Spinning

That the carded cotton needed more preparation for the spinning process would soon be seen as an essential requirement by the factory pioneers. For the spinning machine only drew out the thick strips or strands into thinner ones and any irregularities in thickness in the strands would therefore be reproduced over longer lengths. What was needed was a means of producing more even strands before feeding them to the spinning machine.

Little is known about the preparatory machines which Arkwright used in his early mills. In 1775 he took out a second patent,[5] which purported to include these machines, but the specification is vague and even misleading in parts. He may have done this to deceive his immediate rivals, although when taxed with the evasions he stated that his intention had been to prevent foreigners from copying his machines. Certainly the construction of machinery for use between the carding and the spinning processes would present more difficult mechanical problems than did those concerned with the opening and cleaning machines. In the cottage industries preparation for spinning following carding was usually done by spinning coarse and very soft-twisted slubbings on the wheel, and this system continued to be adopted for some years after the introduction of the spinning jenny in the homes. In actual fact, as explained in Chapters 1 and 7, the jenny-spinner was able to even out many of the irregularities in the slubbings, a result which could not be achieved on Arkwright's machine. So in the mills it soon became evident that a further process or processes was required between carding and spinning if good results were to be obtained. As well as the unevenness associated with the slivers delivered by the carding machine, the fibres in these slivers were still lying in all directions, whereas they needed to be straighter and arranged in near-parallel order to respond satisfactorily to the roller-drawing process. It would also be evident that the transition from a relatively thick strip of carded cotton to a fine thread could not be accomplished efficiently by passing it between three or four pairs of drawing rollers—the ratio of roller speeds would be much too large for good results. Yet if the carded strips were made thinner they would not hold together, unless they were twisted, and the twist would need to be extremely slight, or the strips could not be drawn out further. To meet these requirements various methods were tried. One was that of twisting the strips or slivers as they left the carding machine; another was to twist them as they entered the spinning machine, and yet another was to introduce an intermediate machine between carding and spinning—a machine which drew out the slivers to a thinner condition and twisted them a little.

Arkwright's second patent (really a group of patents in one specification) and other patents taken out towards the end of the eighteenth century and a little later are indicative of some of the difficulties which were being met with by the early cotton spinners. Both Arkwright in his second patent and Robert Peel some years later[6] tried feeding the slivers into vertical cylindrical cans whilst these were revolving to insert twist. This twist had to be so limited for the reasons given that the slivers probably broke as they were drawn from the cans at the subsequent process. A modification of this machine used by Arkwright was the lantern frame, so called because an opening with a door was made in the side of a delivery can, as shown in Fig. 27. The slubbing was taken out from the opening in the side of the can, so preventing any stretching or breaking of the slubbing which might have occurred had it been withdrawn upwards. The slubbing was next wound on bobbins at a hand-operated 'winding block', in which form it was suitable for feeding to the spinning machine.

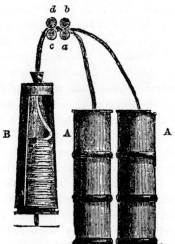

Figure 27   Lantern frame

Although this method prevented sliver or slubbing breakage, it was a relatively costly process because of the manual work involved, and Arkwright continued his search for more efficient methods. He tried a modification of the water frame, but the slubbing proved too

13 Samuel Crompton

14 Replica of Crompton's mule

15 Hall-i'-th'-Wood Bolton

16 Early flat carding machine

weak to pull the bobbin round. A crude variable-speed drive for the bobbins, based on conical drum driving, was presumably tried, since it is described in his second patent, but could not have been a success. Another machine was the jack frame or 'jack-in-a-box'. In this machine again the roving was delivered into a rotating cylindrical can, but inside this was a winding drum which wound the roving on to a bobbin (Fig. 28). It was a complicated arrangement, in which the winding drum rotated on an axis at right angles to the axis of rotation of the can.

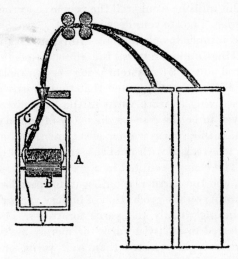

Figure 28 The jack-in-a-box

One intermediate machine which was introduced into Arkwright's early mills, however, was an immediate success. This was the drawing frame or drawframe, a simple machine which by means of three or four pairs of drawing rollers drew out or 'drafted' the carded slivers, combined several of these into one sliver and delivered it into a cylindrical can. The amount of drawing out was roughly the same as the number of slivers combined, i.e. if they were drawn out four times finer, four were merged into one. Hence no twisting was needed to strengthen the sliver, while the drawing-out action tended to arrange the fibres in an approximately parallel order.

Another important result was the production of more even slivers, owing to the combining of several slivers, since the odds were so much in favour of irregularities tending to cancel each other out when brought together by chance. It was found to be so effective that it became the practice to use three drawframes in succession, so that the combination, or 'doublings' as they were termed, with six slivers being joined at each drawing, resulted in $6 \times 6 \times 6 = 216$ mergings. The machine must have had an extremely important effect on the evenness and regularity of the yarn finally spun on the water frame, and it is not surprising to learn that whenever Arkwright discovered or was told of defective or inferior yarns being produced in his mills he would tell the people concerned in his usual forceful manner, 'Look to your drawings!'

His mills continued to operate successfully, at first supplying yarns for the stocking-frame knitters, the round, smooth, full-twisted yarns produced on the flyer system being very suitable for this purpose. About 1773 Strutt suggested that these yarns might also be suitable for weaving as warp yarns in the looms weaving calicoes, and this proved to be the case—a discovery of considerable importance. Previously these yarns were made of linen, cotton yarns having usually been too weak to withstand the strains imposed in the weaving process. The change resulted in a greatly increased demand for cotton yarns, and the partners soon began to specialise—the Belper mill concentrating on the production of hosiery yarns and the Cromford mill spinning mainly the yarns for warps. The latter were generally referred to as 'twist yarns' or merely as 'twist', because they were more highly twisted than weft yarns, and when Arkwright began to spin them they were termed 'water twist'.

This expansion in business resulted in the building of more mills, some in Derbyshire at Milford, Wirksworth, Matlock Bath, and Bakewell, others in Lancashire at Manchester and Chorley, the latter near his home town of Preston. During this period Samuel Need died, and shortly afterwards, about 1781, Arkwright and Strutt dissolved partnership.

Mills were established by other spinners, who used Arkwright's machines under licence, and in the 1780s there were between fifteen and twenty such concerns, mostly situated in Lancashire. Arkwright was now at the height of his prosperity, an extremely busy man who never spared himself or others. He worked long hours and travelled throughout the Derbyshire, Cheshire, and Lancashire areas in a coach and four, using the fastest horses available.[7]

But with rising fortune came further difficulties, involving him in legal battles over his patent rights. He won some of these and lost others, culminating in the famous case fought by the combined cotton spinners of Derbyshire and Lancashire, in the Court of King's Bench in 1785.[8] It was here that Thomas Highs gave evidence about his construction of a roller spinning machine, evidence which was supported by John Kay the clock maker, who assisted him in his work. It was the evidence of Highs in particular which is said to have resulted in Arkwright once again being defeated,[9] although other names were also mentioned as being the true inventors of several of the other machines.

Arkwright was naturally incensed at the verdict, and swore that he would publish to the world descriptions and 'copper plates' of his machines so that foreign countries might compete with the British spinners. He was dissuaded from this action by his friends, and, in fact, the blow, though severe, did not injure him commercially or financially. He was far more experienced and more firmly established in his business than any of his rivals, and so was able to keep ahead of them in technical developments.

He had previously been to Scotland and with David Dale he saw the falls of the River Clyde. He had been impressed by these as sources of power, and the result of the visit was the formation of a partnership between Dale and himself and the establishment in 1784 of the New Lanark Mills. Robert Owen later married Dale's daughter and became the owner of these famous mills, where he carried out many of his reforms. The mills can still be seen, being now owned and used by the Gourock Ropework Company Ltd, a business which was established as long ago as 1736.

Like other pioneers of the times, Arkwright also had his troubles with the rioters and machine breakers who feared unemployment as more mills and machines came into use. Many also objected to being forced by economic necessity to work in mills under strict supervision and for long hours instead of continuing to work in and around their cottages under freer conditions. His mill at Nottingham was burnt down, although in this case the cause was never established. When the Chorley mill, reputedly the largest in England, was destroyed by fire in 1779, however, not only were rioters seen to be responsible but the authorities did little or nothing to quell the mob. The Derbyshire mills were also threatened, but here Arkwright promptly organised resistance, willingly forthcoming from his employees. Cannons were placed in strategic positions around the mills, and small arms and spears were distributed to the male workers, in all from five to six thousand of them. Fortunately the mob, although they had left Lancashire, failed to reach the Derbyshire mills.

He rebuilt the Nottingham mill in 1790 and installed his first steam engine there for directly driving the machines. He had used steam engines earlier in Derbyshire, but these were used only for pumping water in the weirs to higher levels for the water wheels. With steam power and better-constructed machines came higher speeds, which when applied to the bobbins and spindles of the spinning machine produced a shrill whistling sound. So the water frame became the throstle frame, 'throstle' being another name for the song thrush.

The foregoing survey of the achievements of Richard Arkwright is almost sufficient in itself to indicate his character and personality. An outstanding organiser of labour and of machinery processing, he was also persevering, ambitious, forceful, and domineering. At the height of his power he talked of buying all the cotton in the world, presumably to 'corner' it and keep it from his rivals, and even of paying the national debt. Boulton wrote of him, 'Tyranny and an improper exercise of power will not do in this country . . . If Arkwright had been a more civilised being and understood mankind better, he would now have enjoyed his patent.'

He was knighted in 1786, and the following year was appointed High Sheriff of Derbyshire. He died in 1792 at the age of fifty-nine.

CHAPTER NINE

Crompton's Spinning Mule

Samuel Crompton was born near Bolton in Lancashire in 1753, and when he was about sixteen he began to spin cotton yarns on one of Hargreaves's jennies to provide weft for the family hand loom. The jenny had only been invented some five or six years earlier, and was probably a somewhat crude and inefficient machine, so that it is not surprising to learn that young Samuel was very dissatisfied with the quality of the yarn which he spun. If the jenny had been invented earlier and had reached a stage of development at which better yarn could be spun, perhaps the mule would never have been born. For it was his inability to produce better yarn on the small cottage-type jenny which led to Crompton thinking about a better method of spinning. He was then about nineteen.

His first efforts were directed towards improving the jenny and to this end he replaced the clasp or drawbar by a pair of rollers, pressed together by springs. Another and more important change was to mount the row of spindles and a long wood roller or cylinder from which they were to be driven, on to a movable support or 'carriage' running on rails, so that instead of moving the rollers away from the spindles to stretch the yarn, he now moved the spindles away from the rollers whilst the latter delivered the slubbings at a slower rate than that of the carriage movement. Although this change gave him better control of the wire which guided the yarn on to the spindles as the carriage moved inwards, and enabled him to mount the slub-bings on a stationary frame (on the early jennies these moved with the drawbar) the fundamental effects on the spinning yarns were the same as in the jenny. The rollers delivered lengths of slubbings, whereas in the jenny they were released by opening the clasp, but in both cases stretching took place between rollers (or closed clasp) and spindles.

There was, therefore, little or no difference in the qualities of the

71

yarn produced by the two methods—much depended on the skill of
the spinner in each case. But the next development made an enor-
mous difference to the qualities of yarn produced. Crompton,
working secretly at his home all the time, added a second pair of
rollers behind the first pair and devised band and pulley drives so
that the front or original rollers turned three or four times faster
than the back pair. He now had a combination of drawing out by
rollers followed by a stretching process, since he still maintained a
faster movement of the carriage than the rate of delivery of his front
rollers. Because most of the drawing out was done by the rollers,
however, the stretching could now be reduced to an amount which
was sufficient only to even out the yarn. This evening resulted from
the fact that in an uneven length of partially twisted yarn the
thinner portions offer less resistance to twisting and therefore also
resist further attenuation, whilst the thicker, softer twisted places
do not offer this resistance and are drawn out to a fineness corresponding more nearly to the thinner parts of the yarn, as explained
in Chapter 1. It was undoubtedly this feature, coupled with the very
low tensile and frictional strains applied to the yarn during the
twisting operation (compared with the high strains to which the
yarn on the water frame was subjected by bobbin resistance and
flyer friction) which brought success to Crompton's efforts.

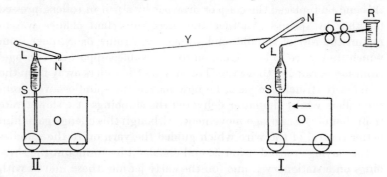

Figure 29   Diagram of Crompton's mule

Fig. 29 shows diagrammatically the essential features of the
machine in so far as they affect the yarn, and this should be compared with Fig. 20, which is a similar representation of the jenny.
The slubbing or roving R, having been drawn out by the rollers E,

passed as yarn Y to the spindle S, mounted on the carriage O. As the spindle rotated to insert twist in the yarn, the carriage moved from the position shown at I in the direction of the arrow, the speed of this movement being greater than the rate of delivery of the second or front pair of rollers. Having travelled several feet away from the rollers, the carriage and rollers were stopped, although the spindles were usually caused to turn for a short time to complete the twisting. The spindles were next made to turn several revolutions in the reverse direction, to remove the coils of yarn on the bare part of the spindle and the wire N attached to levers L brought down to take up the slack yarn, as shown at II. The carriage was now pushed in towards the rollers and the spindles turned in the original twisting direction to wind the spun yarn on the spindle, the wire being used as a yarn guide for this purpose. Plate 14 gives a perspective view of a very early mule in which the parts mentioned above can be seen.

Even at this early stage the mule was obviously a more complicated piece of machinery than the jenny, and called for more action from the spinner. Thus certain driving disconnections and reconnections were needed to enable him to continue twisting after he had stopped the drawing rollers from turning, and again when he was turning the spindles relatively slowly to wind the yarn, at the same time manipulating the wire (known as the winding faller wire) to guide the yarn on to the partly formed 'cop', and then to restart rollers, spindles, and carriage for the next cycle.

Fig. 30 shows the essential features of a much later mule, with three pairs of drawing rollers E, the spindles being turned through bands V from a cylinder T extending along the length of the carriage O. The winding faller wire is shown at N, also a second wire M, the counter faller wire, which rises to take up the yarn uncoiled from the spindle and acts as a tension control during the winding operation.

Did Crompton know that Arkwright was already using the drawing-roller method when he was making his 'wheel'? He finished it and began spinning yarns for his own use about 1778–79, when he was twenty-six, and when the water frame had been in use in Nottingham and Derbyshire for some six or ten years. Had he heard of Paul's machine, patented forty years earlier and used in Northampton, Birmingham, and other places? He denied knowing anything of these 'roller-spinning' machines.[1] Certainly he could not have known any details of Arkwright's drawing rollers with their 'clockwork' gears, or he would not have used the clumsy and unreliable driving bands and pulleys.

Crompton's machine not only spun more even yarns; it spun much finer and softer twisted yarns, again because of the gentle stretching action described. And when he began selling his yarns, it was their fineness, hitherto associated mainly with the hand-spun

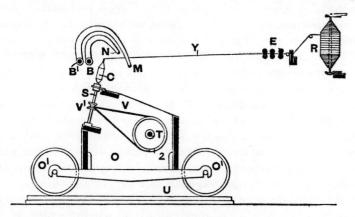

Figure 30   Diagram of improved mule

yarns of India, which confirmed many people's suspicions that he was and had been for some time secretly engaged in the construction and use of a new 'wheel'. At first it was referred to as the 'Hall-i'--th'-Wood' wheel—the name of the house in which Samuel resided with his mother and which is now a museum containing many domestic and other early possessions of the Crompton family. Later it became known as the muslin wheel, because of the fineness of the yarns produced and their suitability for the weaving of muslins. As the machine became better known and it was realised that it combined the drawing rollers of the water frame and the stretching, twisting, and winding actions of the jenny, some wit decided that such a 'cross' should be dubbed a mule, and the name stuck.

The secrecy with which Crompton had worked served only to increase the inquisitiveness of those who had seen the fine yarns, and many subterfuges were employed in endeavours to discover how the machine operated.

Even Arkwright is said to have visited the 'Hall' to find out more about the machine,[2] although this report has not been substantiated. Cotton spinners in the area began to press him to supply them with machines, and it soon became obvious to Crompton that his secret could no longer be preserved. He seems to have been badly advised on the question of patenting his machine—certainly the drawing rollers could not be protected, but the 'spindle carriage' could have been, or so it would appear. Actually, however, he was persuaded to disclose his machine to the world, in return for an agreement, signed by eighty-two interested industrialists, mainly of Bolton and Manchester, whereby an unspecified sum of money from 'every well-wisher of the trade' was to be given to the inventor. The agreement was signed in 1780, but some of the signatories never fulfilled their promises and Crompton received only about £60 in all, for the disclosure of a machine which in due course and with added improvements was manufactured in thousands and made millions of pounds for their owners. Fortunes were made, too, by those who began weaving muslins with the fine yarns.

Crompton's first machine contained between twenty and thirty spindles, and was constructed largely of wood. Even the drawing rollers were made of wood, and one of the earliest improvements was that of equipping the machine with metal rollers and toothed wheels or 'clockwork', as were being used in the water frame.[3] The large driving wheel was probably placed in a vertical position, driving a cylinder extending the length of the carriage, following the introduction of this method of driving on the jenny. The use of metal rollers and structural improvements in general made it possible to make longer machines, containing up to 130 spindles. Another important improvement was that of placing the large wheel and the corresponding driving parts near the centre of the machine instead of at one end. By this method it became possible to operate still longer mules, extending up to 400 spindles, and also making it easier for the spinner to tend more spindles. Later machines carried upwards of 1,000 spindles.

Along with these improvements were others which relieved the spinner from some of the connecting and disconnecting operations referred to earlier, so that in time every mechanical operation of this kind was carried out at the right time automatically; every operation, that is, except those concerned with the winding of the yarn on the spindle. These improvements enabled water and later steam power to be used for the drawing and twisting operations, but the winding continued to be controlled by hand. It was not until between 1825 and 1830 that this operation became automatic, due to the inventions of Richard Roberts, described in Chapter 21.

David Dale was the first spinner to use water power to drive mules at his New Lanark Mills. This was about 1792, and he was probably induced to make this effort because of a patent taken out by William Kelly, the manager of the mills, for an automatic mule.[4]

Crompton's subsequent career was largely one of frustration and disappointment. Always a morose and secretive kind of man, lacking business ability, he became embittered as a result of the disappointments he had suffered at the hands of his fellow men. He knew how the mule was being developed and used successfully by others, he heard of the power-driven machines in Scotland; he read of the large fortune left by Arkwright on his death in 1792 and he grew more embittered.[5] He tried to branch out as a mill-owner in a small way, employing about ten people, but even here his rivals took away by bribery his workers as he trained them. In disgust he gave this up to go into business as a bleacher with his sons. It was about this time that Robert Peel called upon him with a view to taking him into partnership in his growing textile business. Crompton refused the offer, partly no doubt because of his independent nature, and partly, it is said, because of his dislike and distrust of Peel. Yet the acceptance of the partnership could have been an important turning-point in his life. It might have led to larger and earlier developments in the textile industry, similar to those which arose out of the partnership of Arkwright and Strutt, and would certainly have provided Crompton and his family with happier and more prosperous conditions.

To make matters worse, the bleaching business failed through bad management on the part of Crompton's sons, and as old age approached Crompton was in danger of having to live in a state of comparative poverty. Some of his friends helped him from time to time, but even their attempts to obtain some compensation through Parliament and by public subscription were failures. He died in 1827, but it was not until 1862 that a statue in his honour was erected in his native town of Bolton.

Samuel Crompton's invention, improved by a number of later inventors, brought incalculable wealth to the country. Bolton became the world centre for the spinning of the finest cotton yarns, and the finest and most delicate fabrics, woven, knitted, and lace, once owned by a wealthy few, became available to millions.

CHAPTER TEN

Early Carding Machines

Carding is an operation in which fibres like cotton and wool are subjected to the action of surfaces having closely set wire points. This action loosens and partially disentangles the fibres from each other and may be said to be the final stage of the opening out or loosening processes, so that if required the fibres may be readily straightened and arranged in roughly parallel order in the subsequent processes. It was and still is probably the most important of the preliminary processes of spinning; wool in particular required to be hand carded before being spun on the wheel. Cotton, however, was probably not usually carded in Europe until baling was introduced.[1] As already explained, the early inventors of spinning machines soon found that carding machines were also needed.

Figure 31   Hand carding

Before the introduction of these machines, carding was for centuries carried out by means of hand cards. A pair of these is shown in perspective in Fig. 31, and Fig. 32 shows a simplified side view. The lower card was held resting on the knee (the process was sometimes called knee carding), the cotton or wool was placed on the teeth, and

79

the upper card moved over it in the direction shown by the arrow at A. Owing to the inclination of the wires, which were usually set in leather, each surface held some of the fibres, and separation and disentanglement resulted. By turning one of the cards round, as shown at B, the lower card was now 'stripped' of its fibres, the result being a thin film or web of carded fibres.

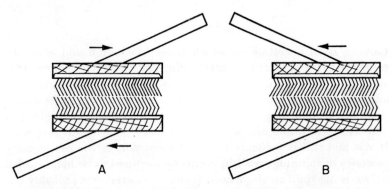

Figure 32　Hand cards: A Carding position B Stripping positions

Various modifications of this method of carding were adopted, the processes in general being termed stock carding, as distinct from hand carding. In one system the lower carding surface was made larger and fixed to a bench, so that the operative had only the upper card to hold and move. In another system, the card was attached in a vertical position to an upright post and the moving card, also now made larger, was fixed to a cord passing over a pulley in the ceiling, with a balancing weight at the other end. In another version of the pulley method a cord extended from the movable card to a treadle and the movement was controlled by the foot of the operator.[2] Although these modifications increased the production, they failed to meet the need for a continuous supply of material for the early spinning machines.

If the periphery of a cylinder were covered with wire points, and the cylinder rotated close to another surface similarly covered, a continuous carding action could be carried out with the possibility of the delivery of lengths of carded material. This, in fact, was the method employed by the two first inventors of carding machines.

The two patents were taken out in 1748, the first by Daniel

Bourne[3] and the second by Lewis Paul.[4] Bourne's machine consisted of a series of small cylinders covered with wire points driven by gearing and cranks. It does not appear to have been a success, although it formed the basis for subsequent machines. Paul's machine, on the other hand, seems to have served its purpose, for he used it in his factories. A perspective view is shown in Fig. 33. He used only one cylinder, B, the other surface, shown at C, being curved to correspond with the cylinder surface. This was movable through levers E and G and handle H. It could be lowered for the cotton or wool to be placed on it, then raised for carding as the cylinder rotated, and again lowered to remove the carded fibres; this stripping was done with a long comb or 'needlestick' operated by hand. The strips so removed in roll form were then joined by hand. Later Paul added a device which joined the strips and wound them on a small roller automatically.

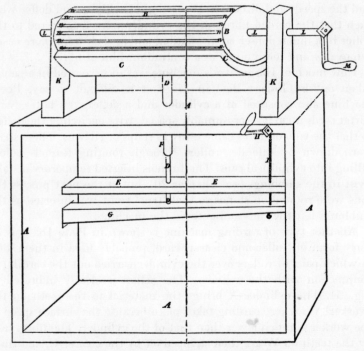

Figure 33   Lewis Paul's carding machine

As mentioned earlier, Hargreaves made stock cards before he invented the jenny and Robert Peel had in mind a machine 'consisting of two or three cylinders' when he asked Hargreaves to make a carding machine for him.[5] This was about 1760 and seems to have been a reversion to Bourne's ideas. But the use of bars or 'flats' in conjunction with a cylinder was also developed, these being placed above the cylinder for ease of access, since each flat could be lifted for stripping.

Hargreaves later constructed a machine the outstanding feature of which was the addition of a smaller cylinder, known as a doffer. This was also covered with wire teeth or points, and was positioned close to the larger cylinder. A machine of this type, with flats above the cylinder, is shown in Plate 16; it was originally used in Arkwright's mills. The cylinder is 32 in and the doffer 16 in in diameter, both being 18 in wide. Later they were made nearly twice this size, and more than twice the width. The inclination of the wire teeth and the speeds and directions of rotation of cylinder and doffer were such that the carded fibres on the cylinder were transferred to the doffer in a much denser accumulation, and as such were more easily removable and maintained as a continuous film of fibres.

How much of Hargreaves's machine was incorporated in a patent taken out by Robert Peel in 1779[6] it is difficult to say. Peel's machine also consisted of a cylinder and a doffer, the latter 'with garter cards upon it'—presumably spaced strips encircling the doffer, so that the web of fibres came away as strips or ribbons. These strips were drawn by calender rollers through rotating funnels before falling into cylindrical cans. The funnels inserted temporary or false twist in the slubbings (see Chapter 20), but at the next process the cans were rotated on stands so that 'true' twist was inserted as the slubbings left the cans and entered the machine.

Another type of carding machine is shown in Plate 18. It is an early form of 'roller and clearer' card, probably used in the 1780s, in which pairs of rollers over the cylinder carried out the carding in conjunction with the cylinder. The action is clearly indicated in Fig. 34. The cylinder A brings the material to the teeth on the 'worker' W, where carding takes place because the surface speed of the worker is much lower than that of the cylinder. The fibres held by the teeth on W are then stripped off by the clearer C, and these in turn are transferred to the cylinder. One advantage of this method of carding over that of the flat carding machine at the time was a saving in labour, since the equivalent to the flats, i.e. the workers, were stripped automatically.

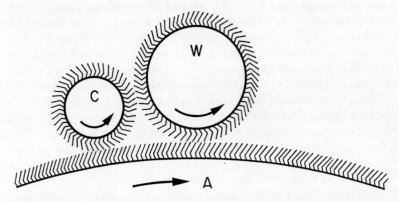

Figure 34   Diagram of roller and clearer

Reverting to Plate 18, the doffer in this machine was situated between the large cylinder and the cylinder D, which was not covered with wire points. The card clothing on the doffer was arranged in widthway strips (unlike that in Peel's card, which had circumferential strips), and as the strips of fibres were transferred to the cylinder D they were rolled into slivers by the grooves which can be seen on the periphery of D. The cranked lever on the cylinder D, looking like a handle, struck an arm of the capstan below at each revolution, and this caused the delivery apron to move forward intermittently.

About 1784–85 Samuel Crompton constructed a carding machine. Unlike most of the machines then in use, the cylinder took the cotton downwards, the carding taking place along the underside (a reversion to Paul's method). He claimed that by this means the impurities fell away. The cotton was then transferred to a doffer. He did not develop the machine further. Instead, in a fit of anger at the treatment he had received when he released the details of his mule to the world, he smashed it up, saying, 'They shall not have this, too!'[7]

Since there was probably much copying and pirating of ideas through the migration of workers between the mills, the various early carding machines so far described would not be restricted to particular mills. In any case, they were in principle based on the patented machines of Paul and Bourne. Arkwright probably used several kinds in the early mills. One of the problems involved was that of automatically removing the film of fibres from the doffer in a continuous length and in a form which did not require the material to be twisted to hold it together. This was finally solved by the invention of the doffer comb, an invention which was claimed by Arkwright. It consisted of a rapidly oscillating comb extending the width of the doffer and set close to it. At each downward stroke the comb removed fibres from the doffer in the form of a film or web which was then drawn through a funnel to emerge as a relatively thick sliver. The invention was also claimed to have been devised by Hargreaves,[8] although the consensus of opinion is that either Arkwright or one of his employees was the true inventor.

In the course of further developments, there seem to have been differences of opinion about the relative merits of roller and clearer cards and flat cards. In some cases a compromise was struck and machines were made in which half the carding surfaces consisted of rollers and clearers and the other half of flats. Improvements were also introduced in the construction of the carding surfaces. Plied woven fabric replaced the leather as a foundation for the wire teeth, and the complete assembly became known as card clothing.

Although these early carding machines were first constructed for the carding of cotton, it was not long before the woollen industry began to use them and to adapt them for the longer and coarser wool fibres. In particular, a modified machine was made having coarse teeth and using only rollers above the cylinder (termed a 'swift' in the woollen industry). The machine was known as a 'scribbler' to distinguish it from the finer-toothed carding machine. There were scribbling mills, in which the wool was first opened out in a 'willy', then passed through a scribbler, followed by a carding machine and a slubbing billy (see Chapter 18), the first three machines being driven by power in the period 1808–14.[9] The machine preceding the scribbler has also been described as a 'plucker', but it is not known whether this was a different machine or merely another name for the willy.

Gradually carding machines became more standardised, with the roller and clearer type mostly used. Fig. 35 shows the sectional elevation of such a machine, in which there are six pairs of workers and clearers. As the lap Q unrolls it passes under the feed roller D to a small-toothed cylinder E (the 'taker-in'), thence to the cylinder A. The doffer stripping comb is shown at K and the delivery rollers at L.[1]L.

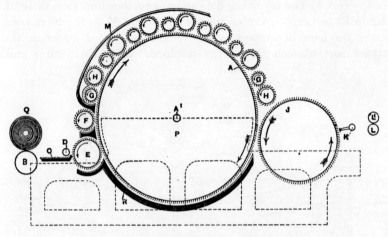

Figure 35 Revolving flat-carding machine

In 1834, J. Smith connected the flats to two endless chains, adding more flats so that the entire series could be moved slowly along curved supports or 'bends', over the cylinder, and taken over the top, where they were automatically stripped and cleaned. They then continued moving to the feed end of the machine, where they once more began to slide over the bends in carding positions. The arrangement can be seen in Fig. 36, which shows a perspective view of what became known as the revolving flat card. The chain of flats is shown at U.U. The invention not only reduced labour costs but was the first step towards bringing the flat card into favour, especially for cotton, since it provided a much greater actual carding surface compared with the roller and clearer card. A further addition to the machine is seen at I, a device which coils the sliver after it has left the rollers L, into a tall, cylindrical can.

Another method of automatically stripping the flats was that of Wellman, of the U.S.A., in 1853. In this system the flats remained as separate units, and at suitable intervals of time mechanism raised each flat from the cylinder, turned it over, stripped it, and returned it to the working position. A similar method was, in fact, patented in Britain in 1823 by A. Buchanan,[10] but does not appear to have been taken up. Certainly in Britain the revolving flat card was preferred even after Wellman's invention, although the latter was popular in the U.S.A. The revolving flat card was further improved in 1850, when Evan Leigh invented the 'flexible bend'.[11] As the term indicates, the bend or support for the flats, extending as an arc on the upper part of each side of the machine, was made flexible and,

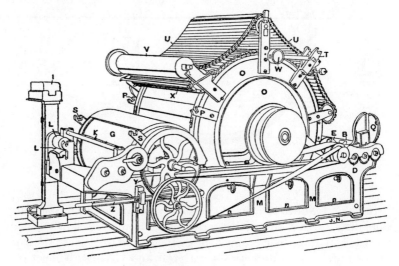

Figure 36   Improved roller and clearer carding machine

therefore, adjustable to a slightly different radius, so that the carding spaces could be adjusted to fine limits between flats and cylinder. These spaces could now be 'set' for different conditions, often to compensate for the shortening of the wire teeth. The latter occurs as a result of periodic 'grindings' to sharpen the points. Because of these and other improvements the revolving flat card became the established machine for carding cotton during the 1880s.

    In general, revolving flat carding machines are now used for cotton, and roller and clearer machines for wool and for cotton-waste processing. Plate 18 is a general view of carding machines in a cotton mill in the early decades of the nineteenth century, and it can be seen that then, as now, other machines as well as carding machines were to be found in the 'cardroom'. On the extreme left are what appear to be lapping machines (see Chapter 8), used to convert the opened cotton into laps to feed to the carding machines. These are also on the left and are of the stationary flat type, with doffers, doffer combs, and delivery or calender rollers which collect the carded web of fibres and compress them into slivers. These fall into cans, but there are no coiling mechanisms. On the right is a slubbing frame producing very large double-flanged bobbins, some of which can be seen on the floor. The size of these bobbins and the height of the frame make one wonder whether the artist has got his proportions wrong. It is obvious that the operatives would not be able to reach the top of the frame, where the drawing rollers are situated, unless there was a raised platform at the back of the machine. It is also rather surprising to see the frame positioned with the delivery side facing the carding machines; normally, to facilitate the 'flow' of the material, the feed side would face the carding machines, so that the card cans need be taken only across the alleyway instead of, as in the illustration, dragged round to the other side of the machine.

CHAPTER ELEVEN

Cartwright's Power Loom

The usual first step towards making a loom suitable for power driving, was to connect all the required movements so that they were operated from one source. Such looms had been invented and used as long ago as 1586, although their functions were limited to the weaving of narrow goods such as tapes and ribbons.[1] Little is known of these early looms, but later improvements included means by which as many as fifty ribbons were woven at a time, instead of the earlier four to six ribbons, although even this small number was an improvement on the one ribbon per weaver produced on the ordinary hand loom.

Since the shuttle, a small one, was required to travel only an inch or two at each pick it was a simple matter to use a series of pegs fixed to a sliding bar to push the shuttles from side to side.

Another method was that of using cog wheels and a sliding toothed rack. A lever manipulated by the weaver was connected to the sliding bar, and the healds all moved together as he also operated the treadles. It was, of course, the limited shuttle movement which made the method possible. The need to make the shuttle travel several feet instead of a few inches made it much more difficult to produce a power-driven wider loom.

The looms were known as Dutch looms or engines, because at one period they were imported into this country from Holland. Many edicts were issued on the Continent against the use of the looms, and in London there was rioting in the seventeenth century over their use and the unemployment they were causing. In Switzerland a means was devised for driving the looms by water power in 1730, but this was prohibited. Thirty years later a mill in Manchester was equipped with similar looms and driven by water power. Joseph Stell, who owned a silk mill in Keighley, also had a number of ribbon looms there driven by water power. Later improvements in the looms led to the establishment of a narrow-fabrics industry using power-driven looms.

Early attempts to produce a power-driven wide loom were all based on moving the shuttle by positively controlled means instead of by a 'throwing' action. Leonardo da Vinci made sketches about 1490 showing an arm carrying a shuttle half-way across a loom, and a similar arm at the other side to which the shuttle was to be transferred to complete the movement. In 1678 de Gennes, a French naval officer, patented a loom in which a similar device was used to move the shuttle. He used crankshafts to raise and lower the healds and a quadrant to move the slay. It was not a success, neither was a loom invented by another Frenchman, Vaucanson in 1745, who also used levers to move the shuttle. These failures were probably due to the slowness of the shuttle movements compared with the quick hand throwing of the weaver. Actually, Kay had patented his fly shuttle some twelve years before Vaucanson's invention, although Vaucanson may not have known about it. According to one authority, if he had known and had adopted it, the power loom might have made its way half a century earlier than it did.[2]

In 1774, Robert and Thomas Barber, of Bilsborough, Nottingham, took out a patent[3] for a loom which 'may be worked by men, horses, cattle, fire, air or water'. The pickers ran on horizontal rods as in Kay's attachment, each picker being connected by a strap to a spring, which was released through a lever connection to a cam in the driving shaft. This cam was formed with a 'sudden curve' to give a quick release to the spring. The slay was moved forward, also by a cam on the driving shaft, but was brought back by a suspended weight. To quote the same authority again, 'this loom was wonderfully near being a solution to the problem conceived and had its inventors possessed the tenacity of purpose of Dr Cartwright, there can be little doubt that their success would have been assured'. The patent was taken out some eight or ten years after the jenny had become known, and five years after the water frame had been patented, so that the need for a power loom to increase weaving production must have become evident and it is surprising that more efforts were not directed towards making a success of the loom. The earlier power loom inventors mentioned did not have this spur towards further efforts, and the new spinning machines, followed by the invention of the mule, with their vastly increased output of yarns of all kinds, at lower costs, presented a major problem to the industry—how to increase loom output.

The general opinion amongst the manufacturers of the day was that the construction of a loom which could be driven by water or steam power was practically impossible. It was argued that there were too many separate and different movements needed in the loom, and all these required timing and controlling in a way that only a skilled weaver could operate. Some comments of this kind were made to Dr Edmund Cartwright, then rector of Goadby Marwood, near Melton Mowbray, when he discussed the question with some Manchester manufacturers, in an often-quoted account of the conversation.[4]

Although he knew nothing at all about the subject, 'having never at the time seen a person weave', he decided to disprove the arguments he had heard by making a power-driven machine which would weave cloth. In due course he succeeded and took out a patent.[5] It wove cloth, but it took two strong men to turn it, and they tired in an hour or two. In his own words, 'The warp was placed perpendicularly, the reed fell with the weight of at least half a hundredweight, and the springs which threw the shuttle were strong enough to have thrown a Congreve rocket.'

He had devised this machine without ever having seen a hand loom, but he now decided to see one and to study its actions and those of its operator. His next attempt was based on these actions, and the loom was patented in 1786.[6] He took out a further patent[7] the following year and yet another[8] in 1788. The basic features involved the use of cams or eccentrics and levers. The specification drawings are badly done, and Figs 37 to 39 are simplified sketches based on them, but modified to make them clearer.

Fig. 37 shows how, by the use of levers and eccentrics, the actions of the weaver's feet were imitated to raise and lower the healds. C and C1 are two cams shaped somewhat as shown with levers L and L1 pressing against their peripheries. The fulcrum of the levers is at F, and, as can be seen, the healds H and H1 are raised and lowered through the connecting cords S and S1. This method of operating the healds is still extensively used, the cams being known as 'tappets'.

Fig. 38 shows the method used (described in the 1786 patent) for throwing the shuttle E. Again he used cams, not the periphery this time, but the side, which was formed with a gradual incline starting from the low position L and reaching the high position at H, on the cam C, when there was a sudden drop to the low position. A pro-

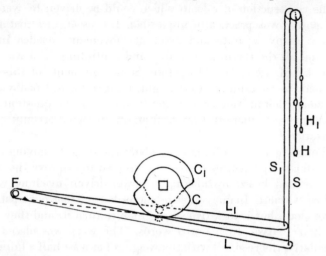

Figure 37 Diagrams of heald connections in Cartwright's loom

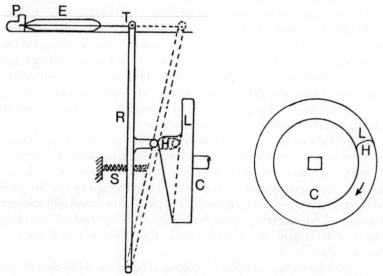

Figure 38 Diagram of picker connections in Cartwright's loom

jection on the lever R, at the side of the loom, was pressed against this face by the spring S. It can be seen that as the cam turned the higher part of the incline would compress the spring, and at L this would cause a sudden jerk of the lever to the position shown in broken lines. The 'picker' P connected by the cord T to the lever would be given an equally violent jerk to send the shuttles across the loom. A similar set of cam and lever at the other side of the loom threw the shuttle back.

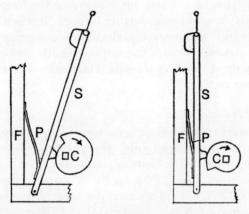

Figure 39 Diagram of slay connections in Cartwright's loom

Fig. 39 shows how Cartwright obtained the to-and-fro movement of the slay. Again he used a cam C shaped to move the slay arms or 'swords' S, but so shaped as to give a very quick return from the forward position. Flat springs P, attached to the loom frame F, kept the swords pressed against the cams.

Although with the above mechanisms applied, say, to a hand loom the machine could be turned by water or other power, and would indeed weave cloth, it still required the almost continuous attention of one person, a circumstance which would have little effect on reducing labour costs. To enable a weaver to tend more than one loom, two other important additions were needed. One was a device which would stop the loom if the weft failed; the other one which would stop it if the shuttle became trapped in the warp shed. These were occurrences which the hand-loom weaver could see and at once stop working his loom, but cloth could be spoiled and warp yarns damaged in a power loom by these occurrences where the weaver was, say, tending an adjacent loom.

Cartwright foresaw these difficulties and added an automatic mechanism which stopped the loom whenever the weft failed, either by yarn breakage or by the emptying of the shuttle. He also fitted a flat spring inside each shuttle box, and connected it to the stopping mechanism, so that if the shuttle was not in its box when the slay was about to move forward, and the spring therefore not pushed aside, a projection on the slay hit a buffer in the loom frame and stopped the slay from moving further forward. It was a sudden and violent stop which was necessary, since even one complete forward move of the slay would force the trapped shuttle towards the cloth and break many of the warp threads. The mechanism was termed a warp-protector motion.

Other Early Power Looms

Whilst Cartwright was developing his loom on these lines and indeed trying it out on a commercial scale, other inventors were working on the production of a power loom, or, as it was sometimes described at the time, a 'steam loom'. John Austin of Glasgow began work on a power loom in 1789, but did not carry his experiments far enough to justify patenting it.[9] Some members of the Glasgow Chamber of Commerce continued developing the loom and in 1798 thirty of the looms were set working at the spinning mill of J. Monteith, of Pollokshaws, near Glasgow. Later this number was increased to 200, all driven from a steam engine, and it was stated that one weaver and a boy could tend from three to five of these looms.[10]

A model of the loom was sent to the Society of Arts in London, and in 1850 this along with other exhibits was sent to University College, London. In 1857 many were sent to the Science Museum, but the loom model was not amongst them. It may have been amongst a number of exhibits which were destroyed at the time.

Another pioneer was J. L. Robertson, also of Glasgow, who set up two looms in 1793, using a Newfoundland dog as the motive power, and later installed forty looms in a building in Dumbarton—what kind of power he then used has not been mentioned.[11] It is evident that during the period under discussion, following closely on Cartwright's experiments, Glasgow was the centre of some intensive efforts towards the construction of a successful power loom, for in

1796 Robert Miller of that town also built a power loom. Unlike some of the other inventors, he actuated the picking stick by means of specially shaped cams or 'wipers' to give the required quick action, and the loom became known as the 'wiper loom'. A front elevation is shown in Fig. 40 which shows that the picking stick L was placed midway between the shuttle boxes and thus the picking action approximated more closely to Kay's method than did that of Cartwright. Again unlike Cartwright, his slay or batten was swung from the top of the loom, along the lines of most hand looms. In this matter Cartwright's was the better method, providing steadier running, and the practice was followed by all the later loom constructors. Amongst the other features of Miller's loom were the slay action, which was thrust back by a cam, but was moved forward by

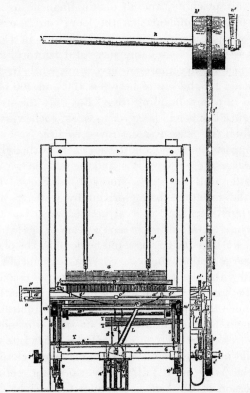

Figure 40   Miller's power loom front elevation

springs (an arrangement reverse to that of Cartwright, and which would give a very quick beating-up action), and a warp-protecting motion. The latter appears to have been similar to Cartwright's, bringing the slay to a sudden stop, but having a wire detecting device instead of flat springs in the shuttle boxes.

Some of the above-mentioned looms reached a state of efficiency in which a boy of fifteen, tending two looms, could weave three and a half times more cloth than one skilled weaver using the fly shuttle.[9]

During this period of activity in the development of a power loom, Cartwright began to try out his loom on a commercial scale. He moved to Doncaster, where he hoped to find more skilful workers to assist him in the construction and working of the looms and in 1786 he visited Manchester with a view to getting the businessmen there interested in his machine, and to obtain financial assistance. He failed to do so and, confident that the loom could be successfully worked, he set up a spinning and weaving mill in Doncaster. It appears to have been a reasonably successful venture, for he later built a larger factory, to contain twenty looms, while in Manchester a firm contracted for the use of between 400 and 500 of his looms to be installed in a new building there. But only the steam engine and about twenty looms had been set to work, each weaver tending two looms, when the place was destroyed by fire. No evidence was available to support the charge, but it was generally thought that local hand-loom weavers were responsible, and the scheme was abandoned.

The Doncaster mill was a four-storeyed building 84 ft long and 25 ft wide, the machines being driven by water power from a tributary of the River Don. A local newspaper at the time stated that on one loom 'a child of six or seven years of age would be able to do as much work in one day as could be done by the older method in a week'. George Crabbe, the poet, who was a friend of Cartwright, visited the mill with his wife. Their son describes her reaction: 'When she entered the building, full of engines thundering with relentless power, yet under the apparent management of children, the bare idea of the inevitable hazards attendant on such stupendous undertakings quite overcame her feelings and she burst into tears.' But the venture did not prosper and in 1793 Cartwright closed the mill, heavily in debt. Why did it fail? Partly, no doubt, because of the crude construction of the looms, although Cartwright did provide the right movements; for a study of the mechanisms he devised points to his having solved several problems connected with the weaving operation, including such important ones as those of automatically stopping the loom on the failure of the weft and on the trapping of the shuttle between the warp threads. Another factor was probably his inexperience of commercial practice. But the main cause of the failure of this and other contemporary attempts at power weaving on a commercial scale was due to a general failure on the part of the inventors and their sponsors to appreciate the importance of so organising the processing that the looms ran with as few interruptions as possible. This aspect of the matter is explained more fully in Chapter 12.

If one considers the backgrounds and training of Kay, Hargreaves, Arkwright, and Crompton, with their practical knowledge and skills, it is indeed surprising that a man with so very different an outlook on life should have become an inventor of textile machines. He was born in 1793 at Marnham in Nottinghamshire, and was the younger brother of Major John Cartwright, the pamphleteer and reformer. He was educated at Wakefield Grammar School and at University College, Oxford, but did not become a Doctor of Divinity until 1806. He was forty-one when he met the Manchester businessmen, and beyond making some improvements to an agricultural machine at his father's home during a college vacation, he had had no experience of machinery or of inventing anything. In fact, his interests were mainly of a literary nature; he wrote articles and poems, and delivered lectures.

His daughter Mary wrote of him: 'There was nothing in the pursuits of the first half of his life calculated to lead his mind to study the theory of mechanics, or in his habits to bring him acquainted with their practical application.'[12]

Even when he became involved in his weaving experiments and in his attempts to make his loom a commercial success, he continued his literary pursuits, and found the writing of verse a consolation when he suffered reversals of fortune.

The Government made him a grant of £10,000 chiefly because of the benefits ultimately gained by the country as a result of his invention of the power loom—actually he estimated that he had spent between £30,000 and £40,000 on developing this and other inventions. He died at Hastings in 1823 and was buried at Battle Church there.

CHAPTER TWELVE

Radcliffe's Dressing Machine

The threads which are to form the warp in a woven fabric require to be prepared before they are placed in the loom. Usually, but not always, they are wound side by side on a roller or beam, so that the beam contains the required number of threads and the warp is of a predetermined length. There are other requirements of a more technical nature, which are intended to simplify the work of the weaver, and these are provided during the process which is known as warping.

In the earlier period of hand-loom weaving this process was carried out by the weaver, usually by 'wall warping'. This involved the use of large wood pegs fixed in a wall, usually an outside one.

The weaver first attached a number of threads to a peg; he then walked along to a distant peg or series of pegs, carrying the threads with him, wrapping them round the final peg, then retracing his steps and repeating the operation until the number of threads stretched between the pegs equalled the number he needed in his warp.

> And now (the weaver) strains the warp
> Along the garden wall or highway side.[1]

The distances between the pegs were spaced to give the length of warp required. He now leased the warp by threading cords in and out of the yarns near the ends of the warp to keep them in their relative positions to each other.

The warp was now ready for removal from the pegs in the form of a 'rope' of yarn, and this he wound into a ball as he walked from peg to peg. 'Warp dressing' followed, a process in which the yarns were spread out in sheet form and wound on the beam, ready for the loom. The fact that the threads had been leased simplified this operation. A method of warping used in the woollen industry consisted in the use of frames known as 'bartrees'. They were 10 ft wide and the yarn was wound to and fro round pegs on them and dried out of doors.[2]

Sometime during the seventeenth century the 'warping mill' was invented, consisting essentially of a large circular frame rotating on a vertical axis. The pegs were fixed at required intervals on this frame, which was turned first in one direction, then in the other, so that the threads could now be wrapped backwards and forwards spirally around the frame with the operative staying in one place. Fig. 41 shows such a mill, along with a stationary frame or 'creel' carrying bobbins of yarn previously wound on a wheel or simple winding machine. The mill shown was operated manually; water power was used later, and it soon became the practice for warping to be carried out away from the weaver's cottage, in a separate building, from which warps were supplied to the neighbouring weavers. Sometimes instead of winding a ball the warp was linked to form a chain as it was unwound from the mill.

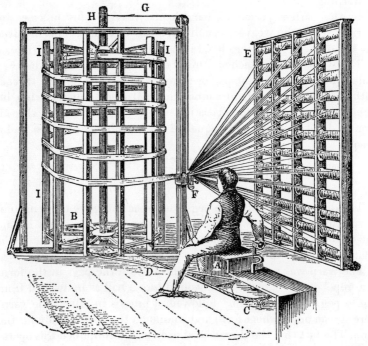

Figure 41 Early warping mill

In order to strengthen warp yarns and to reduce their tendency to fray during the weaving process, it was customary to apply an adhesive substance such as starch paste. This could be done by passing the warp, while still in rope form, through a mixture of this kind and drying it before winding it on the beam. During the subsequent separation of the matted threads in the dressing process much of the dried paste fell away from the yarn, however, and it was usual for the weaver to apply the paste when the warp was in the loom. He kept a supply of the paste, usually also containing tallow to lubricate the yarn, near his loom, and at intervals applied this by means of a brush to the lengths of warp between the beam and the healds. He then fanned the threads to hasten the drying process before resuming his weaving.

This procedure naturally resulted in a considerable loss of production, and William Radcliffe, who owned a mill at Mellor, in Cheshire, where he employed many hand-loom weavers, became concerned about this loss, especially when he began to hear of inventors and others who were engaged in endeavouring to make and to operate looms driven by power, where one weaver could tend at least two looms. Cartwright had, in fact, attempted to minimise this loss of production on his power looms by devising a means of automatically applying the dressing material while the loom was running. The apparatus did not dry the yarns quickly enough, however, and the looms had to be stopped at intervals until the drying was completed. Some other users of power looms appear to have adopted the practice of the hand-loom weavers, stopping the looms at frequent intervals to apply and to dry the dressing. Extra workers were employed in some cases to apply the dressing while the looms were running, the warps in such instances often being only partially dry on reaching the healds.[3] This practice must have caused much clogging of healds and reeds, however, and it is probable that looms were often allowed to stand while the paste dried.

To meet the potential competition of the power looms, Radcliffe decided to try to improve the efficiency of his hand looms. With the help of a skilled and inventive mechanic in his employ named Thomas Johnson, a cloth-taking-up motion was devised which wound the woven cloth on to a roller automatically as the weaver operated his loom—hitherto the weaver had to cease weaving from time to time in order to wind up this cloth by hand. Much more important, however, was the decision to take the dressing operation away from the loom, and to devise a machine which would apply the starch paste to the yarns and dry them.

The machine was patented in the name of Johnson in 1803[4] and improved upon a year later.[5] Radcliffe has stated that Johnson's name was used as being unknown, in order to conceal the invention from foreigners, who would have investigated the patents more thoroughly had Radcliffe's name been associated with it. The combined result of the two patents was the introduction of a beam warping machine and a dressing machine which in addition to applying paste or 'dressing' to the yarns and drying them wound them on to a beam ready for the loom. (This dressing process should not be confused with the warp dressing mentioned earlier, in which the warp, in ball or chain form, was transferred to a beam.)

The beam warping machine wound the yarns on to a beam, these yarns having previously been wound individually on to separate bobbins. A number of these beams were then placed in position in the dressing machine. The system dispensed with ball warping and is now widely used in the cotton industry, although ball warping is still practised for specific purposes.

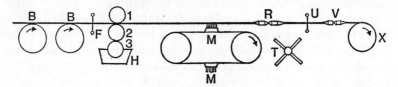

Figure 42   Diagram of Radcliffe's dressing frame

Fig. 42 is a simplified drawing showing a side section of the working parts of the dressing machine. Some of the warping machine beams are shown at B; as the yarns unwound from these they passed through a reed F, then between flannel-covered rollers 1 and 2. Roller 3 was half immersed in the paste in the tub H, and transferred this paste to roller 2. In this way the paste was applied to the yarns and excess paste pressed out. Brushes M on an endless moving belt assisted in spreading the paste evenly and also 'laid' the projecting fibres on the yarns. A fan T hastened the drying process, and after passing over and under lease rods R and V and through a reed U the yarns were wound on the weaver's beam X.

These machines enabled the weaver to work his loom with fewer stoppages, but there was a much more important outcome of the invention. Indeed, it was of revolutionary importance and one which was not anticipated by Radcliffe. This was no less than the application of the system to power weaving, resulting in power weaving becoming a commercial success. As Radcliffe wrote in 1828, after describing how he and Johnson had worked on the machines for two years, 'Had I desisted at this trying point, there would not have been a power loom at work this day in the kingdom.'[6]

One manufacturer has given the following information to illustrate the increase in output following the use of the power loom: A very good hand-loom weaver, twenty-five to thirty years of age, could produce two pieces of shirting in a week. In 1823 a steam-loom weaver, fifteen years of age, produced seven pieces of similar material working two looms. In 1826 the output reached twelve to fifteen pieces per week. In 1833 a weaver aged between fifteen and twenty, working on four looms and assisted by a twelve-year-old girl, produced from eighteen to twenty pieces.[7] It is not stated whether the later increases were due to loom improvements or increasing skills. Probably both factors contributed to the results.

Amongst many who soon adopted Radcliffe's system on power looms were the Peels, the Strutts, and John Monteith. One important manufacturer who did not adopt the system at the time was Samuel Oldknow, who had mills at Stockport and Mellor. Like Radcliffe, he employed a large number of hand-loom weavers, and about 1787 he organised a warping and dressing system on a factory basis. By 1808 he was dressing the warps in rope form by passing them through a tub of paste, then through a wringer, and finally hanging them on rails near a stove to dry. The warps were then taken to the weaver. The methods were, of course, similar to those described earlier and had the same disadvantages, although the systematic organisation and centralisation of the work no doubt gave more uniform results.

Radcliffe's ambition had been so to improve the hand loom that it would continue to be used throughout the textile areas. But he was finally obliged to adopt the power loom in his own business—'the unwilling creator of a factory system in weaving'.[8] He was born in 1761 in Mellor, and as a child learned carding and spinning, producing cotton yarns for the hand looms of his father and elder brothers until he grew old enough to be a weaver himself. Before he was thirty he had established himself as a master manufacturer, and by 1801 he was employing over a thousand weavers.

He was a man of strong opinions, and became very concerned when, as a result of the increasing use of spinning machines, a surplus of cotton yarns could not be absorbed by the hand-loom weavers. Spinners began to export the yarns and Radcliffe, amongst others, feared that this would lead to the decay of the weaving industry in this country. An organised campaign was conducted by a group of manufacturers with the object of restricting these exports— suggestions were even made for them to be prohibited. Although the movement failed in its purpose, the position was soon to be rectified by the successful development of the power loom.

6

CHAPTER THIRTEEN

Developments in Pattern Weaving

The use of cams or tappets to raise and lower the healds in a loom has been described in earlier chapters. In hand-loom weaving these movements, actuated through the treadles, were often limited to two treadles. More were used in many instances—in 1814 there were highly skilled weavers who worked nine treadles,[1] but these were exceptional. With tappets in the power loom, more shafts could be used and with the increase in the number of heald shafts came greater variations in the movements of the warp threads, producing more elaborate patterns in the fabric. When changes in the designs were required, however, changes in the types and positions of the tappets were necessary—a slow and troublesome operation. This was partly overcome by the inventions of special tappets which could be varied in shape. The best known of these was the Woodcroft tappet, invented in 1838.[2] It consisted of a number of detachable sections which could be changed about in the one tappet so as to vary the heald movements.

But there were other methods of actuating the healds which made pattern changing a much easier operation. One of these was an attachment to the loom known as a 'dobby'. Little appears to be known of the early history of this attachment. It was used in some hand looms, and probably crudely constructed versions of it preceded the invention of the jacquard loom. It is of interest to note that another meaning of the word dobby is 'a household sprite or apparition', whilst the attachment itself has also been termed a 'witch' and looms fitted with them were 'witch looms'.[3] There may be some connection between these terms and the impressions of early users of the attachment on seeing the 'magical' effects in the patterns being woven.

James[1] refers to 'a wood machine placed across the loom' in use in Yorkshire during the early years of the nineteenth century and

105

which was probably a kind of dobby. The designs produced on the looms varied from small diamond-shaped figures termed 'birds' eyes' to small flowers, when from sixteen to eighteen heald shafts were used. Dobbies were first used in the English silk industry in Spitalfields, in 1830,[4] although it is generally accepted that a really successful dobby was not invented until 1858[5] in Blackburn, Lancashire, a dobby still referred to as the Blackburn dobby.

There have since been many variations of and improvements applied to dobbies, but the fundamental principle of their actions may be described as the utilisation of relatively sensitive mechanisms to *select* the heald shafts which are to be raised or lowered, whilst providing direct connections to the loom for the actual moving of these shafts.

Among the methods of selection used are pegs in small bars linked together, pegs in a cylinder or barrel, and projecting links in an endless chain. In an early example, patented in 1824, a pegged cylinder was devised, turned by the action of a catch on a pattern wheel, 'which has as many notches round it as there are shoots (picks of weft) in the pattern'.[6]

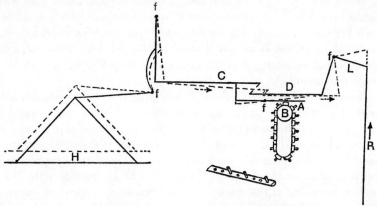

Figure 43 Diagram showing action of dobby

Other dobbies were constructed which were, in fact, small copies of the jacquard machine, but adapted to raise heald shafts.

Fig. 43 is a diagram reducing the parts to their simplest elements, showing the principle on which many dobbies operate. Motion from the loom is given to the dobby through the rod R worked from a crank, and through the lever L the hook D is given a to and fro motion. The barrel B carrying the pegged lags (one lag is shown separately in perspective) is turned to bring a fresh lag into position under the lever A after each picking action. There is a series of these levers, one for each peg-hole in a lag, and when a peg is brought under a lever the latter is raised, resulting in a lowering of the other end. This end is supporting another hook C, which is brought down, and as indicated by the broken lines, the resulting movements of levers (all fulcrums shown by the letter f), the corresponding heald shaft H is raised. Thus a peg inserted in a lag raises a heald shaft and where a shaft is not required to be raised the hole is left empty. (For simplicity, only a part of the complete dobby is indicated in the diagrame. Actually there is another set of hooks above those shown which operate in a similar manner.)

There is, of course, a limit to the number of heald shafts which can be found space for in the usual type of loom. When larger and more elaborate designs are required, i.e. designs involving a greater number of separate movements of the warp threads, it became necessay to dispense with the shafts or to use them as auxiliaries, and to tie together in one bunch all the threads required to make the same movements. Each bunch was then attached to one strong cord which extended upwards to a platform where an assistant could lift and lower them as required by the design. Such looms were known as draw looms and the assistant as the drawboy.

The origin of draw looms is unknown, although they are believed to have been used first in the East for the weaving of silk. The method of weaving was so complicated and relatively costly that its use was mainly confined to luxury materials, and it was in France, the centre of the silk industry in the sixteenth and seventeenth centuries, that many of the improvements were first applied to the loom. An exception was the invention of J. Mason in England, in 1687,[7] by which he claimed to be able to weave draw loom type fabrics 'without the help of a draught boy'. No details or drawings are given in the specification and it is not known to what extent the loom was used. An early improvement to the draw loom was that of extending the cords to enable the drawboy to work on the floor at the side of the loom, and this was followed by the provision of additional cords which simplified the work of selecting the healds. Fig. 44 is a diagram of such an arrangement, in which it can be seen that if one of the cords S ('simples') is pulled down, the corresponding group of healds is raised, since the cords D are fastened to a wall at W. The simples could be held down by passing beads E through holes in the board A and into slits, as shown at E^1. The healds were pulled down when released by the weights T ('lingoes').

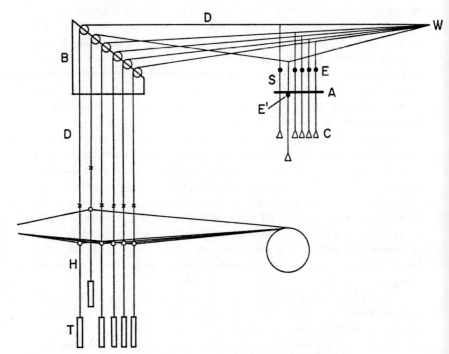

Figure 44   Diagram showing action of drawloom

It is often assumed that J. M. Jacquard first used punched holes in paper as a means of selecting the healds, but this was the invention of Bouchon, a Frenchman, in 1725. Fig. 45 shows in simplified form how the device operated and Fig. 46 is a general view. The simples S were threaded through the eyes of horizontal needles N in a box D, and the needle-ends protruded through the front face of the box. Each simple carried a bead B just below a comb C in the frame G. The drawboy pressed the perforated paper P against the needle-ends before each picking action; a hole allowed the needle to stay in position, a blank pushed it back between the comb teeth. The treadle T was now depressed and the comb box moved down, pulling down the selected simples and raising the corresponding healds, as shown by the broken lines. After picking, the comb was raised, the paper withdrawn from the needles, and the roll of paper turned to

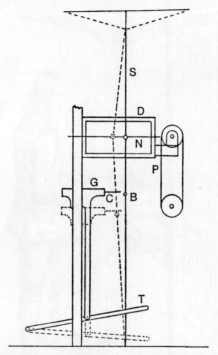

Figure 45   Selection by punched cards, detail

bring a fresh row of holes into position for the next picking action.

Although the drawboy was still needed, the invention was a further step towards the ultimate goal of automatic operation. A later development was that of Falcon, another Frenchman, who in 1728 used rectangular cards instead of a length of paper, and strung them together to form a chain. In 1795 Vaucanson, already mentioned as the inventor of an early power loom (Chapter 11) placed the cards above the loom, so providing direct action on the healds through treadles operated by the weaver. Certain other movements of the mechanism still required the attention of a drawboy and it was not until Jacquard added his improvements in 1801 that the drawboy could be dispensed with. Fig. 47 is a diagram showing how the mechanism operated. The perforated rectangular structure P carried the chain of perforated cards C, and turned a quarter of a

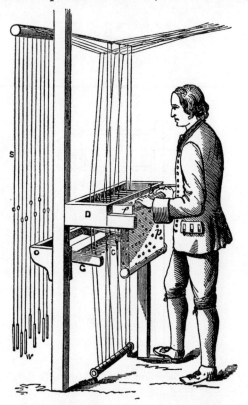

Figure 46   Selection by punched cards

revolution between each picking action. Needles F were pressed against each card at A by the springs S and where there was a hole in a card the needle passed through. Such movements also caused the corresponding hooks E to move to the left as shown at 2, 4, 5, and 7. Bars B below the hooks moved up and down and were so positioned that they only raised those hooks brought directly above them by the needle movements described. The healds were attached to the hooks

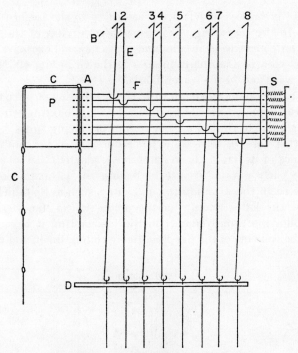

Figure 47   Action of jacquard machine

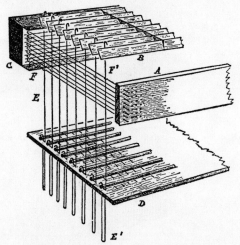

Figure 48   The jacquard machine

and thus were raised or left down according to the pattern of perforations in the cards. Fig. 49 is a perspective view of the device, showing only one row of needles and hooks to avoid excessive detail. A general view of a jacquard 'harness' is shown in Fig. 49. Number 13 is the warp and 14 the woven fabric.

In a British patent taken out in 1817 the selection of warp threads in the draw loom was made by a barrel with projecting wires 'in a manner similar to that of a barrel organ producing tunes'.[8] It was claimed that floral patterns could be produced by its use, but there is no evidence of its having been extensively adopted.

In the early days of its use in Britain the jacquard loom was mainly used in the silk industry, in centres such as Spitalfields and Coventry, the latter mainly for the production of 'fancy' ribbons. Later, following improvements in the mechanism, it began to be used in the weaving of the fine qualities of cotton, linen, and worsted fabrics.

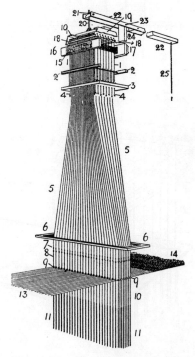

Figure 49   The jacquard harness

CHAPTER FOURTEEN

The Factory System 1

The grouping of a number of workers under one roof to do manual work or to operate machines dates back much further than the Industrial Revolution. At one period a number of relatively large woollen-manufacturing establishments were owned by merchant manufacturers, usually described as clothiers. One of the most famous of these was John Wynchcombe, locally known as Jack o' Newbury. If some verses written about his business are to be relied upon, he employed nearly a thousand people, who engaged in the cleaning, carding, spinning, weaving, fulling, and dyeing of wool.[1] Stocking-frame knitters were also housed in buildings by 'hosiers'. As the industry spread to the Midlands more factories were formed, but since the frames could not be power driven, the main purpose of these buildings was that of preserving the secrets of the processes, and the buildings became known as 'safe-boxes'.[2]

Lombe's silk mill in Derby has been described earlier, this presumably being a copy of earlier mills which operated in Italy. There have also been references to the cotton spinning mills of Paul in Birmingham and Northampton, and of Hargreaves and Arkwright in Nottingham. Hargreaves's mill was a three-storey building, 130 ft long and 30 ft wide in which the jennies were hand operated, while the carding machines were driven from a horse capstan. The building was demolished in 1930, and the site is now occupied by the Nottingham Co-operative Society. A plaque which was over the door of the mill is now in the Hargreaves room of the Society. Arkwright's first mill was erected not far from that of Hargreaves and it was here that Jedediah Strutt first saw the spinning machine. There is some doubt whether a building at Hockley was Arkwright's second Nottingham mill, built in 1790.

The partnership between Arkwright and Strutt was, of course, a vital turning-point in Arkwright's career and had a profound influence on the history of the Industrial Revolution. Without the financial help then obtained, Arkwright's progress might have been long delayed if not arrested and the group of mills which was later established in Derbyshire and elsewhere might never have materialised.

As already mentioned it was at the Cromford and Belper mills that the factory system as it is known today was begun and developed. The invention and introduction of more machines in the sequence of processes converting raw cotton into yarn, described in Chapters 8 and 10, required not only a division of labour, but also some specialisation, since the machines differed from each other and needed different skills to operate them. They also required a disciplined, punctual group of workers which could be assembled at stated times, so that continuity of production could be maintained.

Arkwright's and Strutt's administrative and organising qualities were clearly demonstrated by the successes which they achieved in these early factories. They brought about the required changes in the habits of their employees, and they introduced and developed systems of control and operation without which the succession of processes in the mills could not have been carried out economically, if at all. This achievement is all the more remarkable when it is considered that the inhabitants in the surrounding districts were ignorant, rough, often scarcely civilised—men and women hitherto serving no master directly, working as and when they chose, although generally under the stress of having to earn a living somehow. But the partners did more than build mills, devise machinery, and organise the labour.

> Cromford and Belper . . . were new communities, and their stone and brick-built mills and cottages not uncomely . . . The patriarchal factory village made an appeal to the sense of order . . . They were . . . a deliberate creation, without assistance from the State or local authority and with no public service. The factory, the weirs, the dams, the machine shop, the houses, the roads and bridges, the inn, the truck shop, the church and chapel, the manager's mansion—all were devised and grew up under the owner's eye.[3]

When the partnership ended Arkwright pursued his activities at Cromford, producing warp yarns for the weaving industry, while

17 The Reverend Edmund Cartwright, D.D.

18 Carding machine and slubbing frame, early nineteenth century

19 Early roller and clearer carding machine

20 Masson Mill at Matlock Bath

Strutt at Belper spun mainly yarns for his stocking frames. Strutt had also his silk interests, but Arkwright concentrated on his cotton mills.

As was to be expected, the cancellation of the patent rights released a flood of would-be cotton spinners who began using Arkwright's machines with more or less success. Some existing firms changed from the production of other goods to cotton spinning, e.g. a number of large silk mills in Stockport, supplying yarns to the Spitalfield weavers, made this change. Established cotton-spinning firms increased their plants and became formidable rivals. Amongst these was Robert Peel (the first Sir Robert), whose mill at Bury employed almost the whole of the population of that town at one time, and who later owned mills in some eight other Lancashire towns as well as one in Yorkshire and two in Staffordshire.[4] Peel was an admirer of Arkwright and his methods—'a man who has done more honour to the country than any man I know, not excepting our great military characters'.[5] Peel was also much impressed by the design and construction of Arkwright's mills, and indeed copied them when building some of his own mills. Another successful cotton spinner of the era was John Horrocks, who like many others began his textile career by jenny spinning. He later built several mills in Preston, Lancashire, and brought prosperity to the town, for which he became Member of Parliament in 1802.[6]

Water was still the main source of power, and wherever there were suitable streams the mills and their wheels became features of the countryside. Lancashire was well supplied with such streams, and round about 1788 there were more than forty spinning mills in the southern part of the county. Some cotton mills were also established in Yorkshire and others in the Lake District. Kendal became an important centre, as did Ulverston. The rural surroundings of many of these early factories are exemplified by the illustration of Lord's Mill at Barrowbridge (Plate 21). It was built about 1794 and shows the owner's residence on the left. The rural amenities have been well emphasised by the artist by including both an angler and what looks like a huntsman in his picture!

Developments in Scotland, Ireland and Wales
In Scotland, too, more cotton-spinning mills were established, the forerunners of what was to become an important and prosperous

cotton industry. It was situated mainly in the districts around Glasgow and soon ousted the linen industry there. When Robert Owen purchased the New Lanark Mills he reorganised and modernised them and began producing the finest mule-spun yarns in the world. His autobiography[7] is usually read for the social reforms he brought about, but the book is also of interest for the information he gives about the processes in the mills. Before he was twenty he had become the manager of a cotton mill in Manchester—the first fine-counts mule spinning mill, and during this period he also supervised a mill at Northwich in Cheshire, where water frames were used. Later he controlled the New Lanark Mills for thirty years, and in 1815 was spinning on his mules yarns finer than 300s—the first to accomplish this. It is not surprising that he became known as the Prince of Cotton Spinners. He states that the water frame could spin only relatively long staple cottons from the West India Islands, South America, and the French island of Bourbon (this last was known as Orleans cotton). He adds that no North American cotton was used on the frames; 'it could not be worked up with the machinery then in use'. (Other authorities have indicated that the frames could not produce counts higher than 60s.)[8] When he experimented with the spinning of a sample of Sea Islands cotton sent to him, he wrote that this was 'the first cotton sent from the United States to be spun upon the new machinery through rollers'.

Archibald Buchanan, who invented the card flat-stripping mechanism mentioned in Chapter 10, served his apprenticeship at Arkwright's Cromford mill, and in 1785 established with his father large cotton-spinning mills in Perthshire and Stirlingshire.

In Ireland a successful cotton industry was developed between 1770 and 1820 which at first tended to displace the linen industry in Ulster. In time, however, this success led flax spinners to change to machine processing earlier than they might have done otherwise. Yet this change was retarded by the low labour costs in the country. One manufacturer has recorded that though one machine spinner could produce ten times as much yarn as a wheel spinner, the reduction in cost was only about $8\frac{1}{2}$ per cent on coarse counts.[9] Again, in the finer counts hand spinners could produce yarns six times finer than was possible on the early machines.

In Wales some cotton-spinning mills were started following the example of Christopher Smalley at Holywell. Smalley died in 1782 and an obituary notice in a local paper referred to him as 'the patron and founder of the fortunes of Sir Richard Arkwright'. His son John erected a larger factory, six storeys high, 120 ft long and 30 ft wide. Later most of the Welsh textile industry reverted to the manufacture of woollen goods.

The early spinners using Arkwright's frames drove them by water power, whilst those who spun on the more cheaply constructed jenny, which was not adaptable to power driving, did not need to site their mills near streams. On the other hand, the carding machines they used could be turned by power, and many jenny mills were, in fact, built near rivers. Some of the small cotton mills produced only slubbings on slubbing billies, (see Chapter 18) the slubbings being taken to near-by cottages to be spun on small jennies. Similar systems were adopted when mules began to be used, the jenny taking the place of the billy to supply the slubbings, although it continued to be used as a spinning machine in the woollen industry for many more decades. Improvements in the mule, which was soon producing fine yarns at a much lower cost than that of the imported yarns, led to longer machines being constructed and to partial driving by water power.

All the early textile machines were constructed mainly of timber, as were the water wheels and the overhead shafting and pulleys. There was a gradual transition to the use of iron, and historians are not agreed on the timing of this change. Thus Mantoux states that 'all over the country' wood machines were being replaced by iron in the 1780s and that by 1786 this replacement had been almost completed in the spinning mills. James,[10] however, referring mainly to wool-processing machinery, states that up to 1816 these were made mainly of wood. Yet again, Dobson[11] says that iron framing was not used on textile machines until 1820. He wrote: 'In the construction of the mule, which was the machine Messrs Dobson and Rothwell set themselves out chiefly to make, the work was done mainly by joiners . . . The rollers and bearings were made of wrought iron by blacksmiths in the smithy and the pinions were principally of brass.' The rest of the machine, comprising such parts as the framing, roller beams, carriage, and pulleys, were made of wood. The firm referred to began business in 1790, the name later being changed to Dobson and Barlow, and as the writer would have access to the records of his family firm, his statements may be relied upon.

There are several reasons for the rapid development of the cotton industry, compared with the other textile industries, in the period under discussion. That the early inventions were devised for cotton was one. Efforts to spin other fibres on these machines were not successful, except in the case of the jenny, which, as already mentioned, proved to be very suitable for woollen spinning. Modifications in the cotton machines, as well as the invention of entirely new kinds of machines, were needed for processing the other fibres, and the average would-be spinner had neither time, money, nor ability to carry out this kind of experimental work. He therefore confined himself to the known techniques of cotton spinning. A second reason was the cheapness of the cotton, in spite of its being a foreign product, subject to the additional costs of overseas transport. The third reason was the relative freedom of cotton processing and cotton goods from the statutory controls and restrictions which bedevilled the progress and development of the older-established industries. Large numbers of inspectors were employed in the checking and examination of wool and linen goods to ensure that they conformed to the standards set by the authorities, and although these activities reduced the number of fraudulent practices, and assisted towards the production of good qualities, they also limited the scope of the manufacturers, especially in the development of new ideas, new methods, and new fabrics. The laws to be observed were often old, out of date, and frustrating, and it was because cotton was a newcomer—having no legacy of this kind—that the industry was free to expand and develop.

The Ginning of Cotton

The expansion of the cotton-spinning industry towards the end of the eighteenth century and in the early years of the nineteenth could not have taken place so rapidly had not a young American invented a machine for use in the cotton fields. As the demand for cotton increased the Southern States of America began to grow and to export cotton to Britain. To reduce handling costs it became necessary first to remove the seeds and to compress the cotton into bales. The seeds were removed by a 'gin' (another example of the contraction of 'engine'), which consisted of a pair of wood rollers of small diameter pressed firmly together and mounted in a frame, not unlike a small clothes mangle. It was turned by hand, the cotton being taken between the rollers; the pressure between the rollers was too great to allow the seeds to follow and in this manner fibres and seeds were separated. It was a slow process and as the demand for cotton increased it became a bottle-neck in the industry.

In the 1790s a young American, Eli Whitney, was residing in one of the cotton-growing districts, and was asked by a friend who knew of his skills in handicraft, to try to devise a better machine for removing the cotton seeds. In a few months Whitney, although trained for a legal profession and never having had any inclination towards invention, had constructed a machine with which he successfully separated the seeds from the fibres without injuring either. It consisted of a series of steel discs fitted with hooks on their periphery, the discs projecting through narrow slots in a metal grid. As the discs rotated the hooks dragged the fibres through the slots, leaving the seeds behind. It was patented in 1794 and two years later another inventor substituted saw-like teeth for the hooks. The machine became known as the saw gin and even in the earliest days of its use, driven by a horse and tended by one man, it did the work of more than fifty men working the roller gins. So Eli Whitney should be included in the group of early inventors who speeded the progress of the Industrial Revolution.

CHAPTER FIFTEEN

The Factory System II

The weaving processes continued to be carried out on hand looms for a considerable number of years after spinning machines had become power driven. When Arkwright and Strutt built houses for their workers the houses often had upper rooms or attics in which the menfolk worked hand looms while the women and children were employed in the mills (Plate 23). In some instances, however, the extra room would be a bedroom, since the employers always gave preference to those workers who had large families of young children whom they could employ at low wages. In 1792–93 Benjamin Gott and his partners built a large mill on the outskirts of Leeds in a district known as Bean Ing. It was destroyed by fire in 1799, but was speedily rebuilt. Fig. 50 shows a general view of the mill with its large yard around which were the houses in which the operatives

Figure 50 Park Mill, Bean Ing, near Leeds

lived. These houses, again, contained the hand looms where the yarns spun in the mill were woven into woollen fabrics. It was an efficient combination of power-driven and hand-operated machines which earned for Gott the appellation, the 'Industrial Half-Revolutionary'.[1] As late as 1830, amongst his thirteen hundred employees, all the weavers worked hand looms.

In Scotland hand-loom weaving was a well-established industry which developed rapidly when the fine mule-spun yarns became available. The weavers of Paisley had long been producing silk gauze in competition with the Spitalfields weavers, and their skills enabled them to change to the production of cotton muslins without much difficulty. These same skills led to the production of the Paisley shawl about 1802. The shawls were at first made from the fine cotton yarns, but later spun silk was used and woven into patterns imitating the designs of the Cashmere shawls. John Monteith (see Chapter 12) of Anderson in Scotland was a pioneer in the manufacture of muslins, using mule yarns for both warp and weft, and by 1796 cotton weaving had become Scotland's greatest industry. Yarn merchants and manufacturers employed most of the weavers; they were the 'capitalists of the domestic system' and paid the weavers on a piecework basis.[2] The water frame had made it possible to weave all-cotton calicoes, and now the mule provided British-spun yarns for muslins and other fine fabrics.

Samuel Oldknow visited Cartwright's power-loom mills at Doncaster in 1787, presumably to decide whether to begin power-loom weaving. If so, he decided against the venture, and many of his hand-loom weavers were later transferred to a 'loom house' which he had built near the mill, and which was intended to serve as a nucleus for the establishment of a factory system of weaving.[3] The scheme did not materialise until 1801, when William Radcliffe purchased the mill and began his 'new system of manufacture', a system whereby both spinning and weaving were carried out in factories. The supervision which in this way became possible resulted in improved cloth quality and increased output.

In Ireland the installation of hand looms in factories was not adopted to any large extent in the linen industry, although it was applied in cotton weaving. Thus by 1819 there were fifty-five factories in Belfast and district in which hand-loom weavers were employed.[4]

The Development of Power Weaving

The change from hand-loom to power-loom weaving was at first a very gradual one, partly because of mechanical difficulties and partly because of the opposition of the hand-loom weavers, who held on as long as they could to their independence and their freedom to work as and when they pleased in their own homes. On the technical aspects, Radcliffe, Johnson, and William Horrocks have been described as having done for power weaving what Arkwright did for spinning, and as a result of their contributions more power looms began to displace hand looms. Some were installed in converted rows of cottages; thus in Keighley in Yorkshire upwards of twenty cottages adjoining a small stream were altered to contain power looms driven by a water wheel. In Oldham similar conversions were made with the looms driven from a common steam engine. In Coventry the practice appears to have been to leave the cottages practically intact, using a steam engine which drove overhead shafting which passed through all the houses, driving a jacquard ribbon loom in each house. Rooms in larger buildings were also let along with a power supply to tenants who were the owners of a few looms. This was a practice which persisted for over a century in Nelson, Colne, and other weaving centres in Lancashire. But purpose-built weaving factories were also erected, and these usually took the form of single-storey buildings or 'sheds' with natural roof lighting.

Meanwhile the hand-loom weavers sank into yet lower depths of poverty, some because they persisted in refusing to work in the factories, but many because there was no work for them there.[5] Such of their skills as were still required, attention to thread breakages and replenishment of weft in the shuttles, could be done equally well by women and children. The decline in their condition was all the more distressing since at the beginning of the century they were amongst the most prosperous and well-paid workers in the country. By the 1830s their wages reached such low levels that it became less costly to weave many kinds of fabrics on the hand loom than on the power loom.[6] But as the power looms began to be improved mechanically, in due course their number increased at a greater rate. Between 1813 and 1820 the average annual rate of increase was 2,000; during the next nine years it was 5,000, and during the following four years, 10,000.[7] Most of the early looms were used in the weaving of cotton goods—the increase in their use in the wool industry was much slower. In the linen industry in Scotland they were first used about 1810, but hardly any were in use for linen weaving in Ireland before 1850.

An instance of the active opposition sometimes employed against the introduction of power looms occurred about 1822, when a power loom built in secret by a Bradford manufacturer was installed in a mill in Shipley. The people in the district threatened the destruction of the mill if the loom were not removed, and when subsequently it was taken out of the mill, in the presence of a convoy of constables, the crowd attacked the constables and smashed up the loom.[8]

It was during the second decade of the century that the machine-smashing activities of the Luddites erupted, beginning in the Midlands and extending to Lancashire and Yorkshire. Other writers have dealt fully with this aspect of the Industrial Revolution, and it will suffice here to say that much of the distress experienced by the workers at the time was due to economic crises caused by wars and threats of wars, but, understandably, the factory system was blamed and the outbreaks were often supported by public opinion. Some of the riots in the Yorkshire districts are described in Charlotte Brontë's *Shirley*. It was not until relative prosperity returned to the country that the violence ceased.

Although improvements continued to be made in the construction of the power loom, so that it became possible to weave many fabrics successfully, for many more years the looms proved to be too severe in their actions for more delicate fabrics to be produced on them. Notably, many silk fabrics continued to be woven on hand looms.

The Development of Steam Power

Following James Watt's invention of the rotative steam engine in 1781, it became possible to drive machinery directly from this source. Earlier steam engines had been used in connection with textile mills for pumping water from adjacent streams to higher levels for the water wheels. Arkwright had an engine installed for this purpose alongside the River Derwent in 1780, and at a Bolton mill, which was not sited near a stream, an engine was used to pump water from the mill lodge on to the water wheel.[9] Samuel Unwin used a windmill situated on the roof of his four-storey mill ('Sutton Old Mill') near Mansfield to pump water back into the mill lodge in 1771, and later, when he installed a steam engine, he appears to have retained the windmill, not to save coal, he explained, but to reduce the amount of pollution in the atmosphere. The water wheel, windmill, and steam engine have disappeared and what remains of the building is now used as a silk mill.[10]

The first cotton mill to install a rotative steam engine was Robinson's of Bulwell, in Nottinghamshire, in 1788; but another decade passed before there was any general transfer of power from water to steam. The coalfields of Lancashire and Yorkshire now became the sites for more storeyed mills, while among the Derbyshire hills and dales populations declined and rural conditions began to return. There were other reasons, too, for this move. More labour was available and already housed in or near the towns; there were better transport facilities and nearer markets; and the increasing sizes of the machines needed longer buildings. The narrow buildings planned for the early machines were no longer suitable, nor were such mills competitive against the larger ones.

One of the reasons for the slowness of the changeover from water to steam power was the shortage of skilled men to tend the early engines, which required careful control and regulation, as indeed did the boilers. Carelessness in tending these sometimes resulted in serious accidents and such occurrences probably caused some millowners to hesitate about changing to steam.

The workers on the processing machinery were also subject to injuries through accidents and these became more frequent as machines became more complicated and faster running. Yet it was not until 1844 that a Factory Act was introduced which required the fencing of machinery and the reporting of accidents. Earlier acts had been concerned with the hours of working, the education of children, and the formation of a system of inspection.

But progress continued, and as more steam engines came into use, so began in Britain the era of the tall chimneys, which in the eyes of William Lever of Bolton (later the first Lord Leverhulme) added so much more interest to the northern landscape. Water was still needed for the boilers and this was available in the mill lodges situated alongside the mill. The engine house was usually an extension from the main building, and housed the huge flywheel and the pulsating engine.

As with the machines in the factory, so the steam engines were improved in design and construction. The drive to the mill machines had earlier been through noisy gearing, then by wide leather belts from the flywheel of the engine; still later the periphery of the wheel was grooved to take numerous ropes which drove shafting on the various floors in the mill. The engine house became the pride of the 'engineman', who kept the engine and the whole room in a clean and shining condition contrasting strongly with the heated, humid, and dusty conditions in the mill. He had also the responsibility of lubricating and adjusting the engine to the required speeds and to stop and start it at the correct mill times. Plate 24 shows a typical steam engine and flywheel of the early days of this century which was working in an Oldham mill until a year or two ago.

Other sections of the textile industry had also begun the conversion from water to steam. The Bean Ing mill near Leeds has already been mentioned; the Boulton and Watt engine there was the second rotative steam engine to be installed in a textile factory. Of 40 hp it remained for many years the most powerful engine in Yorkshire. Steam engines were driving cotton mills in Ireland by 1790, but it was another forty years before they were much used in the flax industry there. One of the reasons for the delay was the low wages paid to manual workers, but when the Irish famine of 1845–50 resulted in many weavers emigrating, the subsequent shortage of these workers brought about a general increase in wages; this in turn led to more power looms being used.

The steam engine has now been largely replaced by electrical power. In some instances the mill engine was used to drive dynamos which generated the current. In others the engine was abandoned and electrical power purchased from the local power stations. Large motors in the mill rooms drove groups of machines, then small motors, one for each machine, began to be used. One of the few textile mills still in active use which began with water power, changed to steam, and finally to electrical driving is the Park Green Mill of Messrs Frost Ltd, of Macclesfield, the well-known silk throwsters. The mill was built in 1785 and changed to steam in 1811.

The American Civil War, 1861–65, brought catastrophe to the cotton industry of Britain, which at the time was importing 85 per cent of its total requirements of raw cotton. The other two principal countries supplying the cotton were India and Egypt, and it proved impossible to increase the imports of these cottons except to a very limited degree. Even after the war it was a long time before supplies from America reached normal quantities. There was considerable suffering and hardship, not only amongst the industry's operatives but also amongst tradesmen and others in the districts affected. It has been estimated that the financial losses exceeded £10,000,000.[11] Yet a survey of the number of patents granted during the period relating to textile processes actually shows an increase compared with the years immediately preceding the outbreak of the war. Here is evidence of the determination of the men engaged in the industry to restore it to its former position in the world.

Heathcoat's Lace Machine

Like other inventors who set out to devise machines to do what was being done by hand, John Heathcoat (1783–1861), having decided to try to construct a machine to make lace, began to study how hand-made lace was produced. Broadly, there are two fundamental ways of making lace by hand: the point-lace method and the pillow or bobbin-net method. He decided to apply himself to the latter, perhaps because there were machines in use at the time which made point lace. They were known as point-net machines and began to be used about 1776; opinions differ about the identity of the inventor. They were improved later and about the time Heathcoat began working on his machine about a thousand were in use in Britain.[1] Some authorities believe, too, that a patent taken out in 1803[2] by Robert Brown embodied similar principles to those later applied by Heathcoat.[3] Brown claimed that it made nets 'having the same common diamond mesh and knot hitherto tied by hand with a knitting needle'. It was not a commercial success at the time because fishermen made nets by hand in their 'spare time', yet it embodied mechanical features which were applied later by other inventors.

Heathcoat's first impression on seeing a woman making pillow lace (called also bone lace because bones were sometimes used as bobbins) was: 'A pretty heap of chaotic material I found it, like peas in a frying-pan dancing about!' But more careful observation of the process enabled him to analyse the results as well as to understand the lace-maker's movements. In his own words,

Amongst the earliest things which engaged my attention in regard to the lace, was to ascertain its composition by obtaining a piece of pillow lace. I drew a thread, which happened to draw for an inch or two longitudinally straight, then started off diagonally. The next drew out straight. Then others drew out in various

129

directions. Out of four threads concurring to make a mesh, two passed one way, the third another and the fourth another still. But at length I found they were in fact used in an orderly manner. This process was to answer the question in my mind, can this be done mechanically?

I then saw a woman working on a pillow, with so many bobbins that it seemed altogether a maze. However, I at length perceived that after certain twisting of two, for instance one round the other, and then other two the one round the other, the one of each of these pairs was selected, and they were then made to change places forming a cross, which cross was taken up by a pin, the pin being secured by a hole in a parchment placed to receive it.

After seeing further movements of the bobbins he came to the conclusion that fundamentally there were two sets of threads used.

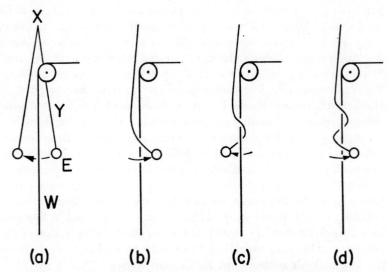

Figure 51   Principle of lace construction

One set always passed forward in a longitudinal direction, while the threads in the other set twisted round those in the first set. Next the threads in the first set moved in pairs, one in each pair to the right and the other to the left, to form the crosses mentioned above and

21 Lord's Mill at Barrowbridge

22 New Lanark Mills

23 Cottages for mill workers at Belpar

24 Engine room of the Magnet Mill, Chadderton, Lancs.

constituting the top and bottom of the meshes in the lace. From this observation he deduced that the former set of threads could be first wound on a roller or beam, to form a warp, all the threads moving forward together, while the latter would have to be treated as individual units, each requiring to be passed round one of the warp threads during its diagonal movement.

He constructed a crude framework and fastened the 'warp' threads in straight rows within it. He wound other threads individually on bobbins and these he passed in and out between the fixed threads, wrapping each bobbin thread round successive lengths and taking it diagonally across the frame. In short, he produced a piece of pillow lace, but by making a 'warp' of one set of threads his method was less complicated.[4] The principle of part of the action is shown in Fig. 51 where a cord Y is suspended from a point X and caused to swing round the warp cord W. The four stages of the movement show that cord Y has made a complete revolution or twist round

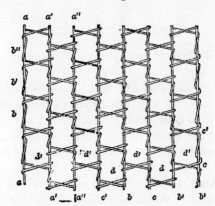

Figure 52 Bobbin-net lace making with taut warp threads

cord W. Fig. 52 shows the bobbin threads twisted round the warp threads and laid in diagonal directions. If the warp threads were held taut, the effect would be as shown. By suitable tension controls of both sets of threads, however, the fabric is given a lace-like appearance, as shown in Fig. 53.

From this simple beginning Heathcoat evolved his lace-making machine, though not without much study and experiment extending over some years. His first patent, in 1808,[5] was a failure. He

destroyed the machine and patented another in 1809,[6] and this
which became known as the bobbin net or bobbinet machine (later
the plain net machine), was soon established as a success. Unlike the
openwork fabrics produced on knitting machines, it produced a
fabric which was an exact imitation of the thread movements of

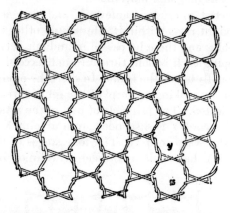

Figure 53   Bobbin-net lace making with warp threads relaxed

hand-made lace. To do this he had to solve two major mechanical
problems—how to carry individual threads round other individual
threads; and how to cause each of the first set of threads to be laid
diagonally across the fabric, half to the right and half to the left.

The warp threads were first wound on two rollers or beams and the
beams were arranged in the machine so that the threads moved
downwards as they unwound. The other threads he wound on
specially made bobbins which resembled discs, since they were very
narrow, with closely set flanges between which the threads were
held—one thread on each bobbin. These bobbins, known as brass
bobbins, were held in narrow holders or carriages, which in turn
rested in a grooved structure or 'comb', in two rows. Situated at one
side of the vertical warp threads, these carriages and their bobbins
were given a pendulum-like movement, causing them to pass
between the warp threads. These warp threads were then given a
side movement so that on the return 'swing' the bobbin threads each
passed round a warp thread. The warp threads were then moved
sideways in the other direction to complete the wrapping or twisting

action. In short, the actions were similar to those of the cord Y in Fig. 51. In addition to these movements, each row of bobbins was given a lateral movement, one row to the right, the other to the left. The movements continued in the same direction, so laying the threads diagonally across the fabric as the warp moved downwards.

To obtain these movements required complicated mechanisms which Heathcoat finally constructed, and he was highly praised by many engineering experts for the excellence of his machine. It formed the foundation of an extensive lace industry,[7] producing fabric which was an exact imitation of what was known as Brussels lace.

John Heathcoat went into partnership with two others and between them they had installed and were successfully running a number of bobbinet machines in Loughborough when, in 1816, the factory was broken into by Luddites, who destroyed fifty-five machines and burned the lace on them. This was a severe blow to the partners and they sued the county of Nottingham for damages. They were awarded the sum of £10,000, conditionally on the sum being spent locally. Heathcoat refused to accept this condition, which implied that the partners should restart their business in the Loughborough area and provide employment for the local people. He said his life had been threatened and he would take himself and his machines as far away as possible from the scenes of destruction in the Nottingham area. To go north at the time would have meant risking his business in another danger area, and having dissolved the earlier partnership he decided instead to go to Tiverton in Devon.

He bought a large mill situated on the banks of the River Exe and installed in it 300 machines to be driven by water power. He transferred a few of his best workers from Loughborough, but in the main drew upon the local people, who had been employed in the dying woollen industry there. Before many years had passed the business was prospering, and it grew in size and importance through the century.

Although his name is associated mainly with the invention of the bobbinet lace machine, he took out other patents including one for a machine for plaiting or braiding and another for the reeling of silk from the cocoons. In 1825 he brought out two patents[8] for the mechanical ornamentation or 'figuring' of lace fabrics. He acquired a sound knowledge of French prior to opening a lace factory in

France, where the machines were run by steam power. It proved a successful venture, lasting many years.[9]

There were many improvements and developments by other inventors in lace-making machines following Heathcoat's success. In 1813 John Lever and some partners introduced a lace-making machine which was not patented because the makers were under the impression that additions to or improvements in an existing patented machine could not be protected. The merits of the new machine, however, were such that experts are certain protection would have been granted. Certainly the machine was a great success and Lever's lace machine is known today wherever there is a machine lace-making industry. It was particularly applicable to the production of designs in the lace, and the Jacquard principle was adapted to this end.

An adaptation of the bobbinet machine was invented by Livesey in 1886. Instead of the bobbin threads traversing diagonally, they were made to run longitudinally except where designs were being formed. The machine began to be used extensively in the making of curtain fabric, and is generally referred to as the lace-furnishing or curtain machine.

CHAPTER SEVENTEEN

The Silk Industry

The silk industry is broadly divisible into two sections, each utilising its own type of raw material, and each producing yarns by machinery and processes entirely different from the other. One section, the silk-throwing industry, produces nett silk yarns; the other, the silk-spinning industry, produces spun silk yarns.

Silk throwing has been described in Chapter 3, and the principle underlying the actual throwing or twisting operation is the same to-day as it was in Lombe's Derby mill. The machines, however, are now much simpler in construction; instead of huge, circular constructions, they are now long and narrow, rectangular in plan, and the spindles are belt-driven from pulleys or drums inside the machines.

As already mentioned, the expiration of Lombe's patent rights was followed by a rapid expansion of the silk-throwing industry. By 1791 there were eleven throwing mills in Derby alone. In 1785 Charles Roe had founded the industry in Macclesfield, erecting the mill in Park Green mentioned in Chapter 15. Soon there were at least twelve mills in the town, which was to become well known for its silk production. In 1810, George Courtauld established a silk factory at Braintree in Essex, beginning as a throwster and later adding a weaving section. His son Samuel began weaving silk crepe fabrics about 1825 and is usually considered to have been the true founder of the firm of Courtauld's, later to become world famous in the man-made fibre industry.

Manchester, Salford, and the surrounding districts also soon became centres of silk throwing—in 1836 there were about 4,700 employees in the industry in that area.[1]

Silk Spinning

The spinning of silk is a process which utilises waste silk, consisting of cocoon remnants from the reeling process, damaged cocoons, and rejected fibres from other processes. Also, there are silkworms which are not of the *bombyx mori* variety—they are not 'cultivated', nor do they feed on the leaves of the mulberry tree. Their cocoons are un-reelable and the silks obtained from them are known as wild silks, one of the best known being tussah silk, from which tussore silk fabrics are made.

All the above types of cocoons are first reduced to masses of fibres by crushing, softening, and cleaning processes; they are then roughly comparable to raw cotton or wool in the sense that the fila-ments or fibres are relatively short and entangled and can be pre-pared and spun into yarns. But first the gummy substance present in these silks must be at least partially removed.

Silk spinning has been carried out for centuries, by hand combing or 'dressing', and spinning by suspended spindle or wheel. The dressing was done by holding portions of the waste and drawing it several times through inclined teeth projecting from a bench or table. The shorter fibres remained embedded in the teeth, the others became straightened and roughly parallel. The silk was then reversed in the hand and the other end combed in the same way. These longer fibres were then laid together ready for spinning.

In 1671 Edmond Blood patented a method of spinning waste silk,[2] but no details are given of the method he employed. Lewis Paul, in his first patent for a spinning machine, refers to the 'engine' being suitable for spinning 'wool, cotton, waste silk as well as other fibres', an indication that silk spinning was a domestic industry here, in the early years of the eighteenth century.

When machinery began to be used in the spinning of cotton, and some knowledge of the machines became more generally known, attempts began to be made to spin waste silk on them. The first successful results appear to have been at a mill near Lancaster in 1792 and later others followed in both Lancashire and Yorkshire, including some which were already spinning cotton. Throstle frames and mules were used, both drawing out the material by means of drafting rollers. Roller drawing, however, could be satis-factorily accomplished only where the fibres were of roughly uni-form length, a condition which was not to be found in the waste silk, since the dressing operation removed only the very short fibres, those retained for spinning being of varying lengths. It was there-fore found necessary to cut the fibres so as to obtain a large proportion of fibres of equal length. Machines resembling chaff-choppers were used for this purpose.

But even 'waste silk' was becoming valuable and it was important that the best possible utilisation of the fibres should be made. What was needed, therefore, was a system of spinning in which widely varying fibre lengths could be used. (The jenny may have been tried, but since it could not be power driven it would not have met the full requirements of the industry.) Gibson and Campbell, of Glasgow, patented a machine in 1836 which successfully accomplished this operation.[3] It was found, however, that the action of the machine was based on that of flax-processing machinery (see Chapter 19) and some parts of the patent had to be disclaimed. Actually, several silk spinners had been using the flax machinery for some years. Other sections of the patent were new, however, and were successfully applied, so that in due course the industry became divided into short-spun and long-spun systems of spinning.[4]

Generally, however, the uncut fibres continued to be combed by hand, and the early attempts by Samuel Lister to carry out this process by machinery is told in Chapter 25. This was about the year 1859, but as early as 1821 a machine was patented in France by Bauwens and Didelot which combed or dressed silk waste, a machine which they appear to have used successfully in a factory they owned in Paris, using a steam engine to drive it. The silk was held by grippers on a table; above was an endless belt to which were attached downward-pointing comb teeth. As the belt moved the teeth combed the fibres, removing the longer fibres first. At intervals the table was raised a little and shorter fibres removed. This graduated action allowed the operator to remove separate deliveries of fibres, each containing fibres of similar length, resulting in an accumulation of several qualities or 'drafts' as they were later called, according to their approximate fibre lengths. By this means it became possible to spin several qualities of yarns, including stronger or finer ones from the longer fibres.[5] De Jongh of Alsace invented a dressing machine in 1856 which was said to be self-acting, i.e. the selective actions of combing and the delivery of the different qualities were carried out automatically.

Meanwhile Lister, having failed to construct a suitable combing machine, reverted to hand combing, but later turned his attention to the idea of 'dressing' the waste and of separating the qualities

automatically. He patented a machine of this type in 1877.[6] Fig. 54
shows a side elevation and Fig. 55 a plan of the machine, taken from
the specification. The two endless belts A carried the silk between
them and held it while another endless belt to which combs I were
fixed moved alongside. These combs passed through the projecting

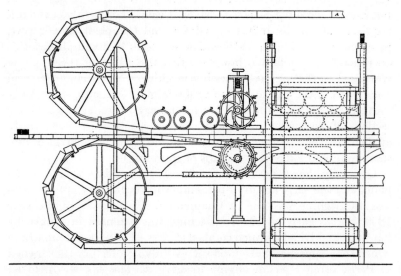

Figure 54   Early automatic silk dressing machine, side elevation

tufts of silk, taking out the shorter fibres, The distances between
combs and tufts decreased as the belt moved, so graduating the
combing. The tufts were automatically reversed after a given
number of combings so that the other ends could be combed. Lister
claimed that his machine was the first self-acting dressing frame,
although this cannot be substantiated in view of de Jongh's earlier
patent.

Later developments in silk dressing included what became known
as the flat dressing machine which embodied to some extent the
principles underlying the action of Lister's machine. It was so-
called in contrast to circular machines which were first developed on
the Continent and were later used in England. They all provided the
graduated combing and separation of the silk into qualities, and
these qualities were numbered. With improved machinery and

techniques the terms long-spun and short-spun ceased to be used, and the draft numbers now indicate the various qualities, draft number one containing the longest fibres.

Because they are made from relatively short fibres whose ends tend to project from the surface, interrupting the reflection of light,

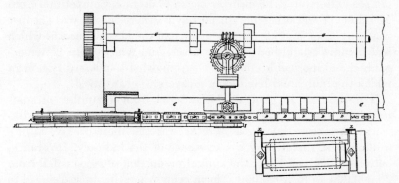

Figure 55   Early automatic silk dressing machine, plan

spun silk yarns are not so lustrous as the smoother nett silk yarns. To reveal more of the natural lustre it is the practice to singe off these projecting fibres. The process is known as gassing. Two inventions patented in 1868[7] combined the process of gassing with a cleaning process which removed the charred fibres and other impurities from the surface of the yarn.

Spun silk is also known as schappe silk, a term originating on the Continent and applied at first to yarns made from waste silk which has been partially degummed by fermentation. The practice has been almost entirely discontinued and the term is now applied generally to spun silk yarns and fabrics.

The Weaving of Silk

Loom developments described in other chapters apply also to silk looms. The jacquard loom was quickly accepted, as the draw loom had been before it, because of the large and beautiful designs which were a traditional feature of silk fabrics. Spitalfields was the most important centre of the silk-weaving industry in Britain, an importance greatly increased by the arrival of Huguenots in the years immediately following the revocation of the Edict of Nantes in 1685.

The houses were specially constructed for the looms, the weaving room itself being usually on the upper floors, with wide windows to let in the light, and double doors to prevent too much noise reaching the domestic quarters below. Towards the end of the eighteenth century there were about 30,000 workers engaged in the industry, but soon afterwards the number began to decline. Competition from Macclesfield and other provincial towns where labour was cheaper was one cause; another was the growth of the larger concerns which had become established in other areas, and which were better organised and more efficient than the somewhat haphazard system in which the individual hand-loom weavers were involved.

The industry in general also suffered from a number of commercial crises. Some of these were the result of diseases of the silkworm. A disease known as *pebrine* was the most deadly, killing millions and threatening the existence of the industry. In France, between 1853 and 1865, the annual production of cocoons fell from 26,000,000 kg to 4,000,000. Alarm grew when the disease spread to other European countries and to the East. Many attempts were made to find a remedy without success. In 1865 Pasteur began his investigations into the causes of the disease and within three years he had isolated the bacilli. He then recommended the selection, rearing, and frequent checking of small groups of worms, and where these proved to be free from disease (which was found to be due mainly to the unhygienic conditions under which silkworms in general were being reared) the distribution of their eggs to the commercial breeders. The measures proved successful and within a few years prosperity was restored—a striking example of the influence of scientific knowledge and methods on an industry.

Import duties on nett silk yarns curtailed foreign competition in Britain until 1826, when certain relaxations were made. This apparent blow, however, acted as a stimulus in the home industry, and machines and methods began to be improved. (One authority at the time stated that 'no machinery in Britain was so barbarous as that in the throwing trade'.)[8] The improvements helped the industry to maintain its level of prosperity.

A much more severe blow was struck by the Franco-British Treaty of 1860. Before that year imports into France of silk, wool, and cotton goods made in Britain had been prohibited. The treaty now allowed the importation of these goods subject to a duty not exceeding 30 per cent, but at the same time allowed similar goods made in France to be imported here free of duty. Its effects on the British silk industry were disastrous. The wool and cotton industries, well established here owing to the relatively early use of machines, were able to hold their own. The French silk industry, however, with a longer tradition behind it, had been earlier than the British in the introduction of machines, their workers were more highly skilled and in particular their fabric designs were far superior—a feature which was of the greatest importance in a luxury article, but not so important in the wool and cotton industries at that time.

The imported silks not only included fabrics of high quality and superior design, but in the lower qualities they were cheaper than the British silks. In the Spitalfields district, where the industry had existed for nearly two centuries, the actual weavers were the chief sufferers, though others in the district engaged in the industry continued to prosper. These, ironically, were the 'masters', who posed as manufacturers, and employed the weavers, but who were merely warehousemen, in a position to begin selling the French silks instead. They filled their warehouses with these goods (stocks were piled in the French warehouses ready for the day the treaty became operative) and did better business than they had done before.

Coventry was another centre, famous for its ribbons, which suffered severely from the operation of the treaty. It was here that Thomas Bird at one time employed two thousand weavers who, from 1770 onwards, wove their ribbons on the Dutch looms.

Many efforts were made to persuade the Government to make modifications in the treaty so as to enable the industry to survive, but without success. Cobden no doubt spoke the thoughts of the Cabinet of the day when he said, 'Let the silk trade perish and go to the countries to which it properly belongs.' It came near to perishing not only in the centres mentioned but in other parts of the country where the throwing, spinning, and weaving of silk had become established, and it was many years before the industry began to recover.

The Woollen and Worsted Industries

The essential difference between woollen and worsted yarns lies in the arrangement of the fibres. In woollen yarns these often lack straightness, and lie in all directions, some roughly parallel with the yarns, others crosswise at varying angles, and many of these with their ends projecting from the yarn surface. In worsted yarns the fibres are relatively straight, and are arranged in approximately parallel order with the yarn, so that the fibre ends do not project much. Woollen yarns are also usually more softly twisted than worsted yarns. In short, woollen yarns are fuller, softer, and rougher in appearance than worsted yarns, which are more compact, harder, and smoother.

The selection of wools has some influence on these characteristics, but the manner of processing is the principal factor. Combing, described in Chapter 23, is mainly responsible for the straightening and parallelising of the fibres. It is a process which was applied to all wools which were to be spun into worsted yarns, but was omitted from the sequence of processes in the production of woollen yarns. Again, the combing process removes the shorter fibres, resulting in greater uniformity of fibre length, so that the wool is more suitable for roller drawing. The rejected shorter fibres are often mixed with wools in woollen spinning, and, indeed, fibres other than wool are also added; obviously, such a mixture of fibres could not be drawn out satisfactorily by drawing rollers—a further factor which tended to leave the fibres in a criss-crossed condition.

An important difference between cotton and wool is that of wax content. Wool contains a considerable quantity of this substance, which is removed by washing, originally by hand, later by machinery. After drying, however, some oil must be applied to lubricate the fibres and so facilitate further processing. This again was at first a manual operation, later carried out by mechanical spraying.

143

The mechanisation of wool processing followed that of cotton. As one authority wrote, 'It was in fact the adoption in the West Riding of Yorkshire of the steam engine and the adaptation of the machines which had given so vast an impulse to the cotton trade to the processes of the woollen and worsted manufacture, that led to the final transfer of those trades from Essex, Suffolk and Norfolk to the former county.'[1]

The Woollen Industry
Wool fibres differ widely as between different growths and qualities and in general are longer, coarser, more intractable, and so more difficult to control than cotton fibres. So, when attempts were made to spin wool on machinery constructed for the processing of cotton, various difficulties were encountered. There was one important exception, however; the jenny proved to be an excellent machine for spinning woollen yarn. It was used extensively both in homes and in small mills over a long period of years. Carding machines had to be modified, however, and much coarser and stronger wire teeth were used. In fact, the changes required for the preliminary carding processes (for it was found that more than one passage through a carding machine was needed) were so drastic that the machine was given another name—the scribbler. This, too, was used in the small mills and was often driven by water power. One or two people could produce as much carded wool on these machines as eight to twelve hand carders, and jennies of from 100 to 200 spindles produced as much yarn as eight to ten domestic spinners using twenty-spindle jennies.

As Paul, Arkwright, and others had found difficulties in establishing a continuation of production between the carding machine, delivering either a wide film or web of fibres or narrow strips as described in Chapter 10, so the early woollen spinners were faced with the same problem. It was temporarily solved by the introduction of a machine which became known as the slubbing billy, one of which is shown in Fig. 56. The widthwise strips of carded web were removed from the carding machine by an oscillating knife or comb and passed into grooves in a slowly rotating cylinder lying parallel with the front of the carding machine. These grooves rolled the strips into rope-like lengths, and as they were delivered children joined successive lengths by rubbing or rolling them and placing them on the feed apron of the billy. Although the machine had the general appearance of a jenny, there were differences; the spindles were mounted on a carriage D which moved towards and away from the clasp, an idea taken from Crompton's mule. Near the clasp was a roller resting on the feed apron B, and the lengths of carded web were laid side by side on this apron, one to each spindle. As the strips

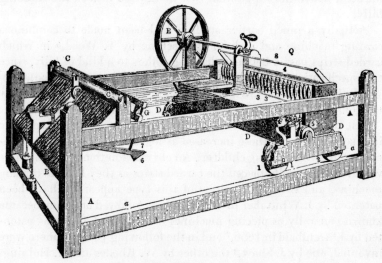

Figure 56 The slubbing billy

moved forward, further strips were pierced to their ends by children, while a man at the other side moved the carriage to draw out the slubbings and turned the spindles to insert a little twist in them.

It was an operation requiring skill and judgement and, like the jenny, the machine was not adaptable to power driving. In the Yorkshire woollen districts lengths of 8 or 9 in of strip were often drawn out to about 70 in.[2]

The mule began to be used for the spinning of woollen yarns early in the nineteenth century, and because of the widely varying fibre lengths, the drawing rollers were dispensed with, rollers only being retained to deliver the slubbings at the required speeds. It has been said that this woollen mule led to the introduction of the slubbing billy;[3] another authority has suggested that J. Swindells of Stockport was the inventor, although there is no definite evidence to support this view.[4]

Swindells was well known as an inventor at the time. He had realised the need for a means to provide continuity of carded material for the spinning machines, and to this end he invented a machine which was a combined carding and slubbing unit, producing slubbing direct from the carded strips. It proved to be mechanically too complicated, hence the supposition that he devised instead the slubbing billy.

Actually a much earlier attempt had been made to combine a carding machine and a slubbing machine by T. Wood,[5] in which carded strips passed between drawing rollers to a kind of billy, since the specification states that 'the spinner advances the spindles towards the clasp'. Like Swindell's combined machine, it was probably too complicated, since there is no evidence of its being used.

But the slubbing billy was not the true answer. It was expensive in labour costs, and these increased as legislation restricted the employment of very young children. An obvious solution was a machine which automatically pieced the carded strips as they left the carding machine, and the first machine of this type appears to have been patented by J. Whittaker in 1827.[6] Others followed and they became known generally as piecing machines or 'tommies'. One was patented by J. Archibald in 1836,[7] and in the following year two more were invented, one by J. Shaw,[8] the other by W. Rhodes and R. Hemingway.[9]

In general the piecing machines operated as follows: as the rolled strips of carded web left the grooved cylinder each was fed to a trough V-shaped in section. As each tray received its strip it moved away from the carding machine and delivered the strip on to an apron which travelled at right angles to the machine: this conveyed the strips to rubbing aprons, the delivery of the strips being so timed as to provide an inch or two of overlap at the ends. They were then wound on bobbins which when filled were taken to the spinning machine.[10]

In 1822, J. Goulding of the United States invented a method of dividing the carded web longitudinally and twisting the strips to consolidate them into slubbings. The dividing was carried out by covering the periphery of the doffer with separate rings of card clothing and spacing these rings apart by rings of leather, so that instead of width-way detached strips leaving the card the strips were continuous and did not require piecing.

25 John Heathcoat

26 Marshall's Temple Mill, Leeds

27 Mules in a cotton mill in the early nineteenth century

28 Heilmann's cotton combing machine

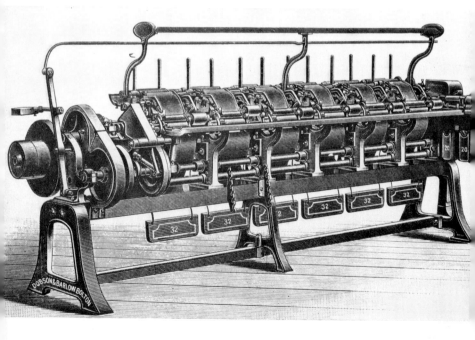

The strips were passed through rotating tubes and wound on bobbins, and although the twist was false it sufficed to compress the fibres together. Some years later the tubes were replaced by two rubber-covered rollers extending the width of the carding machine and between which the strips passed. The rollers were also given reciprocating movements in opposite directions, so rubbing the strips, probably in a manner similar to that used on the piecing machines. The strips were then wound on bobbins ready for taking to the spinning machine. The whole attachment became known as a condenser, and yarns prepared in this manner are termed condenser yarns.

The system does not appear to have been used in Britain until after 1850, and was not used in the woollen industry here until 1870, when wide leather belts or aprons replaced the two rollers. This time-lag is the obvious explanation for the invention of more piecing machines. Thus one was patented in 1840 by E. Leach,[11] the inventor for some reason reverting to the false-twisting tubes in place of the 'endless twisting strap or belt'. Further patents were taken out at intervals between 1848 and 1863, after which the less complicated condenser carding machine came into use.

In 1861 C. Martin of Verviers devised another method of dividing the carded web into strips. He dispensed with the ring doffer and instead passed the whole web between a set of endless leather belts or tapes. These travelled round cylinders, one method being shown in Fig. 57 where W is the web as it leaves the carding machine, F a line showing the passage of one tape and B a broken line showing the

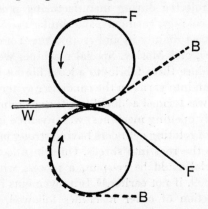

Figure 57 Passage of tapes in the tape condenser

passage of an adjacent tape. These tapes, which may be only $\frac{1}{2}$ in in width, are set close together across the width of the cylinder. It will be seen that tape F crosses from the top to the bottom cylinder and B crosses from the bottom to the top cylinder. Alternate tapes move in the same direction. As tape F reaches the bottom centre position of the upper cylinder it holds that part of the web against the lower cylinder. Similarly, tape B holds the web against the upper cylinder. So the web is split into a series of narrow strips which adhere to the rougher surfaces of the tapes (rather than to the smooth cylinders) until they are removed by the rubbing aprons, the tapes continuing their passages and returning to the cylinders. The mechanism is known as a tape condenser.

The use of jennies continued in the woollen district well into the nineteenth century; mules began to replace them, but it was not until the middle of the century that the self-acting mule came generally into use. In the woollen districts of Wales jennies continued to be used until a few years ago.[12]

The fabrics produced from woollen yarns, as was to be expected, have in general the characteristics of the yarns; some are soft to handle, others rather harsh, depending upon the quality of the wool; all are 'full' with a surface 'nap' of fibres. Typical examples are blankets and tweeds.

The Shoddy Industry

The shoddy industry manufactures textile goods from 'wastes', i.e. from the fibres rejected during manufacturing processes or more generally from wool rags, garments, and similar goods. The industry in Britain is centred mainly in and around the Yorkshire towns of Dewsbury, Batley, and Morley. Special machines were constructed to tear up and reduce these fabrics to a loose fibrous condition prior to their being spun into yarns on the condenser system. One of these machines which was termed a 'devil' (another example of the use of this term for early opening machines) was invented in 1801. It consisted of a series of rotating cylinders having strong projecting metal teeth which tore the rags into shreds. Once in a loose fibrous condition the material could be re-spun, a process which was being carried out by 1809, if not earlier.[13] Improvements in the machine and the introduction of other machines followed, including one which was constructed on the lines of a carding machine, but with the working surfaces covered with saw-like teeth. In 1859 C. Garnett devised a method of inserting these teeth, in strip form, in spiral grooves cut in the surfaces;[14] the machine became known as a garnetting machine and the teeth as garnett wire. It now became possible to tear up much more firmly constructed fabrics, and the trade became divided into two sections—one for the production of yarns and fabrics from the fibres obtained from knitted and loosely woven fabrics, and the other for the production of yarns and fabrics from fibres obtained from firmly constructed fabrics. The fibrous materials became known respectively as 'shoddy' and 'mungo'.

About 1854–55 a process of carbonisation was discovered by which it became possible to utilise fabrics made from mixed fibres, still producing all-wool yarns and fabrics from them. The process destroyed the cotton and other vegetable fibres, leaving the wool undamaged. In general these and other developments in the shoddy industry led to the introduction of cheaper all-wool clothing. There is a comparable cotton-waste industry where processing wastes and cotton rags serve as the raw materials, and in which condenser carding and spinning converts these into yarns of a soft, loose texture which are generally used as weft.

The Worsted Industry

As the jenny was not suitable for the spinning of the more highly twisted and smoother cotton warp yarns, so in the wool-manufacturing districts the machine did not prove to be a satisfactory one for worsted yarns. This would be known to Arkwright and, no doubt, led him to try to adapt his throstle frame to the spinning of these yarns. He claimed that if this could be done worsted yarns would be produced at half the cost of other methods. One of the first changes to be made on his machine would be to space the drawing rollers further apart to accommodate the longer fibres, and this, in turn, would have the effect of reducing control over fibres which happened to be much shorter than his spacing or 'setting'. In fact, the general intractability and 'springiness' of many kinds of wool fibres would make it difficult in any case to control the fibres passing from one pair of rollers to the next. This difficulty is evident from the various attempts made at the time by inventors to control the fibres, as indicated in their patent specifications.

Arkwright has described how one of his managers tried to overcome the difficulty by 'altering the shape (of the rollers) that is, round on one side and flat on the other so that twists get under and betwixt them at a certain time'.[15] Further details are not given, but one possibility is that the top (or bottom) roller of the front or faster running pair was made flat at one part of its periphery, as shown in

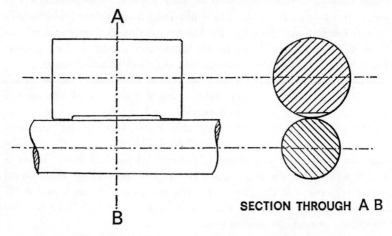

Figure 58   An attempt to draw out wool fibres

Fig. 58. Each time this flat portion reached a position facing the other roller, the gap would momentarily allow twist already in the yarn which had left the rollers to flow through, so tending to control and hold the fibres together. Nothing is known of the outcome of the idea, but even before this time Lewis Paul in his first patent had also tried to introduce twist between his drawing rollers, although the wording of his specification is not very clear.

In 1834, P. Fairbairn patented an arrangement consisting of a revolving tube placed between the drawing rollers. The tube inserted a 'middle' or 'false' twist in the material.[16] As stated in the specification, it was 'a well-known contrivance . . . for twisting and untwisting any roving passing through it', and as has been mentioned was used much earlier by Goulding. (A further description of this form of twisting is given in Chapter 20.)

Another method of controlling the fibres between drawing rollers was shown at the Paris Exhibition of 1855. The top drawing rollers were made to traverse short distances from side to side as they revolved, so partially twisting the fibres round each other. Yet another method was that of using pairs of smaller rollers between the drawing rollers, the upper rollers being very light so that they tended to hold the fibres in their straightened conditions without interfering with their movements through the drawing rollers.

The most effective way of controlling the fibres, however, was that of introducing moving rows of steel teeth, which applied a combing action. These toothed bars or combs were known as gills and were used first in the processing of flax. The bars were linked together by chains, as shown in Fig. 59. The fibres were fed to the gills at A and taken on to B, whose gills moved at a faster rate, so combing and straightening the fibres.

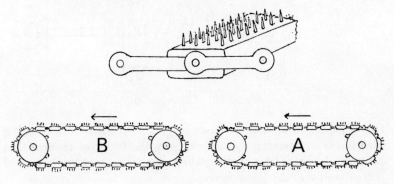

Figure 59   The chain gill

When applied to the gilling of wool only one set of chain gills was used, with one pair of rollers feeding and another pair drawing the fibres through the gills at the delivery end. Later the chains were replaced by screws or spirals, an invention by Lawson and Westby of Leeds, in 1833.[17] Fig. 60 illustrates the principle; the wool was fed between the rollers on the right to the gills, whose ends rested on a pair of screws. As the screws rotated they carried the gills at a higher speed than the rate of feeding by the rollers. On reaching the delivery rollers on the left, each gill in turn moved down on to the lower screw, to be returned and raised to the starting position. As the delivery rollers moved at a faster rate than the gills, further combing took place at this point. Because of these downward movements the gills became known as fallers.

The invention gave better results in the form of straighter and better-combed fibres, and began to be used in the flax and spun-silk industries. It also added much to processing efficiency, and proved to be of outstanding importance. A further development was the invention of the intersecting gill by Green and Warburton in 1851.[18]

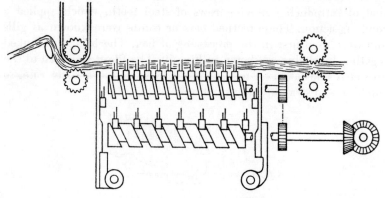

Figure 60   The screw gill

This consisted of an additional set of gills with their teeth pointing downwards and moving above the other gills. Their use ensured that the upper layers of fibres passing through the machine were combed as thoroughly as the lower layers.

A variation of the gilling action was brought about by the introduction of a rotating cylinder in place of the moving bars. The periphery of the cylinder was covered with inclined teeth and the speed of these teeth was higher than the delivery rate of the feed rollers, but slower than that of the succeeding pair of rollers. The method was first applied in France and Belgium about 1856, and the preparatory system embodying the porcupine roller, as it is called, is known as the Continental system, although it is now used also in Britain and elsewhere. Fig. 61 shows a side elevation of the essential machine parts, with arrows indicating the directions of movements.

Arkwright does not appear to have succeeded in adapting his spinning machine to spin worsted yarns, but other spinners did so, although little is known about any modifications which they may have made. In 1788 Brookhouse used what has been described as a modified throstle frame, but there is no patent to be found in his name, nor in the name of his employer, Coltman, at the time, so that it has not been possible to obtain any details of the modifications.

Brookhouse had a number of machines constructed and installed in a factory in Leicester, but before they had been given a fair trial they were destroyed by a mob. He left the district, set up more

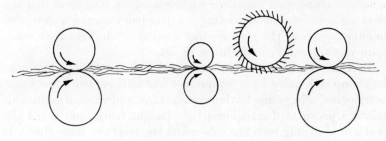

Figure 61 The porcupine roller

machines in a mill in Warwick, and soon made a fortune. Other mill-owners in Leicester also transferred their worsted spinning activities to Yorkshire, using throstle frames as modified by Brookhouse.[19] The machines continued to be used for the spinning of worsted yarns for several decades. Even in the 1850s James lists the machines used at the time in a typical worsted mill in Yorkshire as being mostly throstle frames, with a few mules. The mules were used to spin certain softer qualities of worsted yarns, and they are still used for this purpose.

The Weaving of Worsteds

Although by 1800 the factory system had become established in the worsted industry, the weaving of worsted fabrics by power did not become general until much later, being some years behind the cotton industry in the development.

There had been a similar delay in the adoption of the fly shuttle amongst the hand-loom weavers. In fact, it was not until machine-spun yarns became available that it began to be used. The explanation is to be found in a statement by a hand-loom weaver: 'I was not able to weave a piece a week with handspun (warp) . . . but with machine spun I could weave a piece a day.'

A 'false reed' invented about 1800 appears to have been of considerable help to the weavers. It consisted of a row of vertical wires suspended behind the normal reed, and acted as a clearing device preparatory to the warp yarns passing through the reed. Again to quote a weaver: 'If I had been offered the best cow in England instead of my false reed, I could not, poor as I was, have accepted the offer.' It is not definitely known who was the inventor. It was only needed where machine-spun yarns were being used, an indication that the device was a means for separating rough or hairy yarns which tended to cling together. The reed was not needed for the smoother hand-spun yarns, nor for cotton, linen, or silk.

In 1825 a worsted manufacturer visited the United States to follow up an inquiry for light summer coats. He returned and made samples including some having cotton warps and worsted weft. This mixture provided the required light-weight fabric, but posed the problem of dyeing both the cotton and the wool the same shade. It was some years before satisfactory results were achieved, but by 1837 the fabrics had become extremely popular. Not only light in weight, they were also attractive, and much cheaper than the all-worsted fabrics.

The resulting large increase in trade throughout the Yorkshire worsted industry lasted for many years.

CHAPTER NINETEEN

The Flax and Jute Industries

The Flax Industry
The fibres of the flax plant are extracted from the plant stems, where they form an inner bark. They vary in length from 2 to 3 ft (·61 to ·91 m), but are divisible into smaller fibres, known as ultimate or cell fibres; these vary in length from $\frac{3}{4}$ in (1·9 cm) to $1\frac{1}{2}$ in (3·8 cm). They overlap each other and are held together by gummy matter to build up the longer or 'commercial' fibres.

After lifting, the plants are subject to a coarse combing to remove the seed pods. They are then 'retted' to separate the fibres from the woody parts of the stems, a process usually carried out by prolonged immersion in water, when natural disintegration takes place, leaving the textile fibres undamaged. After drying these are ready for cleaning and preparing for spinning.

For many years during its early history the Irish flax industry suffered several setbacks, and it was not until the eighteenth century that some degree of organisation was achieved, following the lines of the early woollen and cotton industries in Great Britain. At first working independently in their cottages, linen weavers in time became employed by 'masters' and weaving began to be carried out in factories.

The successful introduction of mechanical cotton spinning around Belfast between 1770 and 1820, mentioned in Chapter 14, led to attempts at spinning flax on the same machines. But flax fibres are so different from cotton fibres that even drastic modifications in the cotton machines proved useless. An obvious way of trying to utilise cotton-spinning machinery was chemically to remove the gummy matter, so that the flax was transformed into a cotton-like mass of fine, short fibres. The process was described as 'cottonising' the flax, and was tried in the 1770s. But flax cell fibres, although approximating in fineness and length to cotton fibres, lacked the natural cohesion

155

of the latter, and the experiments failed, as did later ones carried out during the American Civil War, when it was hoped that cottonised flax might replace cotton in the idle mills of Lancashire. The method tried at this time was one devised by the Chevalier Clauson and is described in the eleventh edition of the *Encyclopaedia Britannica*, Vol. 10, page 486.

About 1750 the manufacture of thread was begun in Ireland. In the early years women in different parts of the country began this work on their wheels, and later the industry became organised with one woman in a district giving out work to other women, who twisted several yarns together on their wheels to produce the threads. Still later the work was transferred to factories, the first important venture being that of John Barbour, begun about 1784. This was in Ulster, as was the thread factory of Robert Stewart, and both businesses developed successfully.

But the mechanisation of flax spinning and improvements in the looms were only tardily developed. Even the fly shuttle was not introduced into Ireland until 1776, and was not readily adopted by the linen weavers. As late as 1807–09 premiums were being offered to the weavers to encourage its use.[1] It is not surprising, therefore, that linen manufacturers were soon in difficulties when the cheaper machine-spun cotton yarns became available. The worst blow of all came when 'water twist' began to replace linen yarns as warp in hand looms, and the modernisation of the industry became an urgent requirement.

Scutching, a preliminary opening and cleaning process, was done by hand for many years. A bundle or 'strick' of flax straws was gripped in a frame and the projecting part beaten with a wood beater. But before 1740 the operation had been partly mechanised in Ireland; rotating arms, turned by water power, struck the flax held in a frame as before. Hackling or heckling, which followed scutching, was a coarse raking or combing process carried out by striking the flax with a hackle (a block of wood with projecting steel spikes, about 6 in. [15·2 cm] long), and pulling this through the flax. In 1795 Sellers and Standage[2] patented a method of hackling in which the flax was pulled by hand through stationary, vertical teeth, a method also used to comb waste silk (see Chapter 17). Much more significant was a patent taken out by A. Thompson, of London, in 1801.[3] This was the chain gill (Fig. 59) described in Chapter 18, and

of which a more complete illustration is given in Fig. 62. Later a
heckling machine was constructed in which the straws hung downwards and were heckled by teeth moving horizontally below them,
the whole being arranged gradually to increase the depth of the
combing.

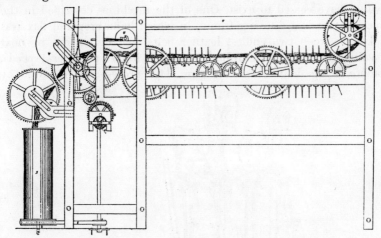

Figure 62   Thompson's chain gill

But the more important problems to be solved before flax could
be machine spun related to preparatory machines later in the
sequences of processing and to the spinning machine itself. The first
breakthrough was the invention of two machines by Kendrew and
Porthouse, of Darlington, in 1787,[4] two names 'indissolubly associated with the introduction of flax-spinning machinery'.[5] The first
of the two machines prepared the flax for the second or spinning
machine, and by a process of drawing out straightened the fibres and
reduced the sheet of material fed to it to a thinner condition. Large
leather-covered cylinders in contact with rollers controlled the fibres,
the ratio of drawing-out speeds being about 3 : 1. In the spinning
machine similar methods were used applying a ratio of up to 8 : 1,
the twisting and winding of the yarn being accomplished by the
usual bobbin and flyer system. A mill was equipped with the
machines at Darlington, but was a failure, although soon afterwards
a mill at Adel, near Leeds, similarly equipped and driven by water
power operated successfully.

In 1790 Matthew Murray, an exceptionally brilliant engineer-inventor (he built a steam-driven locomotive in 1811, several of which functioned for years on the Middleton railway), patented flax-processing machinery[6] which was so successful that it has been said that without this patent the flax-spinning industry in Leeds would have ceased to exist. One of the machines described in the specification is a drawing frame, in which hand-prepared flax was taken between two endless leather belts, and drawn out by next passing through a pair of rollers rotating at higher peripheral speeds, before being delivered into a can. This process was followed by

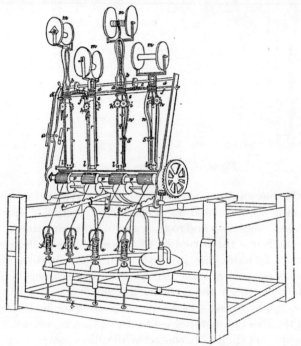

Figure 63   Murray's flax spinning machine

further machines, drawing out the material in a similar manner and winding the strands on bobbins. These were termed roving frames and it should be understood that in these machines the distances between the slower- and faster-moving belts and rollers varied between 2 and 3 ft, i.e. corresponding to the fibre lengths being processed.

In the spinning frame the leather belts were placed *over* the delivery rollers and for some kinds of yarn a machine similar to the one shown in Fig. 63 was used. Here each structure carrying a roving bobbin M and a belt R rotated about a vertical axis, twisting the strand slightly before it passed between a pair of faster-moving rollers P. After the final drawing each strand was twisted and wound on a bobbin as shown.

Although Murray's machines were successful in spinning the coarser linen yarns, they failed to produce the finer counts, which had still to be hand spun. This limitation was at least partly due to the relative coarseness of the long fibres.

Yet the gummy substance holding the cell fibres together could be softened by water, and while so softened the long or commercial fibres could be drawn out or stretched as the loosened cell fibres slipped further apart. Obviously this also increased the fineness of the long fibres. In Murray's machines no provision was made for this wetting.

Wet Spinning

The first man to patent a machine for the wet spinning of flax was Philippe de Girard, a Frenchman who brought his invention to Leeds because he could not interest his countrymen in it. A British patent was taken out in 1814 in the name of H. Hall. [7] The essential features of the machine were three rollers half submerged in a trough of water. The rovings passed between and under these rollers to be wetted, making them (to quote the specification) 'more lax, and the fibres slip past each other with greater ease'. The drawing rollers were set 4 in (10.16 cm) apart for this purpose. The invention, however, was not an immediate success.

In 1825, James Kay of Preston, Lancashire, also invented a system of wet spinning, [8] although in this case two separate machines were required. He had discovered that the relatively short period of immersion of the flax in Girard's machine did not soften the gummy matter enough, and in his first process, carried out in a macerating machine, the flax, after being drawn and slightly twisted by methods already in use, was collected in cylindrical cans which stood in troughs of water. Perforations in the cans allowed the water to pass into them and when the filled cans were taken from the machine they were allowed to stand several hours to ensure the saturation of the flax. The second machine was a spinning machine with the usual flyers and bobbins, but the pairs of drawing rollers were set only about $2\frac{1}{2}$ in (6·35 cm) apart. The method proved very effective, since the cell fibres could now be drawn further apart by the closely set rollers. Kay later brought actions for infringement, and although he won the case for the macerating machine, he lost that for the spinning machine on the grounds that a specific distance between the drafting rollers, such as he had given in his specification, did not constitute a patent. Before long, however, even the macerating machine was discarded, for it was discovered that hot water so speeded up the softening process that the preliminary steeping was unnecessary, and the process of wet spinning reverted to the principle introduced by Girard, but with heated water in the trough.

Some Early Flax Mills

The man associated with Murray in the development of flax spinning in Leeds was John Marshall, Murray having joined his firm as a foreman mechanic in 1789. Together they installed Murray's machines in a mill at Holbeck, near Leeds. At first driven by water power, supplemented by a Newcomen steam engine, a year later a 28 hp Boulton-Watt direct-driving steam engine was used, and by 1893 there were 900 spindles in the mill. The two men went on improving and developing the machines until a large and successful business was built up in the Leeds area, and the town became an important centre, not only of the flax-spinning industry but also of the machine-making industry for flax processing.

The machine spinning of flax gradually spread to other parts of England and at one period there were flax mills in Manchester, Bolton, and Preston, all centres of the cotton industry at the time. Similar developments took place in Scotland. In Ireland there was probably little or no mechanical spinning of flax before the end of the eighteenth century. Even by 1811 there were only twelve flax-spinning mills in Ulster, all of them water driven. In 1829, John Mulholland, who had been a cotton spinner, started a small flax-spinning mill in York Street, Belfast, using the wet-spinning system. The venture grew into one of the largest and most widely known flax mills in the world.

John Marshall's business also grew rapidly in Leeds, his most publicised achievement being the building of the Temple Mill in

1830. Originally, like many other early mills, its surroundings were rural, but as Leeds grew in size the building became surrounded by other property. It was built in the style of an Egyptian temple, with an immense chimney 'like an elongated pyramid',[9] and is said to be described in Disraeli's novel *Sybil*. There the interior is described as 'a single room, spreading over nearly two acres and holding more than two thousand workpeople'. The ventilating system is also mentioned as being 'not unlike that which is practised in the House of Commons'. Actually the likeness to an Egyptian temple applies only to the two main facades which face east. Plate 26 shows the main entrance block. The roof lighting came through sixty-five large glass domes, each 13 ft in diameter. The roof was also originally used as a meadow with grazing sheep, an idea of Marshall's to preserve the rustic scene. After an animal had fallen through one of the domes on to a machine below, however, the practice was discontinued. When first erected the mill was the largest of its kind in Europe, employing 2,300 people. It has also been described as 'one of the architectural romances of the mid-nineteenth century', and as 'a poem in itself'. Perhaps it was a challenge, an answer to Blake's 'dark, satanic mills'. Certainly its fame spread widely and it was visited by thousands of sightseers.

Power-loom weaving in the linen industry came into general use at a later date than was the case in the cotton and wool industries. In 1788, A. Robb invented a power loom for the weaving of linen, and in 1810 J. Crompton took out a patent for the same purpose, but neither loom was a success. Power looms were weaving linen in London from 1812 to 1813, however, and in a factory in Aberdeen 200 looms were producing linen fabrics by 1824–25. These were exceptional cases and probably only the coarser fabrics were produced, for in general some difficulties were met with in the power weaving of linen. These were mainly due to the inelastic nature of the yarns, a well-known characteristic of flax. When warp yarns are raised or lowered by the healds in the loom, so that they no longer lie in a straight line between the back rest (a bar above the beam) and the reed, they are subjected to strain. If they are sufficiently elastic, they will stretch; if not, they will either break or strain the healds or other parts of the loom, as happened on the early flax power looms, where rigid mechanisms could not provide the gentler controls and flexibility provided by the hand-loom weaver.

To quote an early writer, the problem was solved by the use of a roller 'which comes and goes as the heddle moves up and down and prevents any irregular strain on the yarn'.[10] The roller, known as a vibrating roller, extended across the loom and was positioned under the warp threads between the beam and the healds. It was given an eccentric movement so that when the healds were all at their centre positions it deflected the line of warp upwards, and as the healds moved to lift or lower the threads, so the roller turned clear of the warp. In short, the threads were maintained in a deflected line throughout and sudden strains were avoided. Although specially effective for the somewhat inelastic linen yarns, the device proved useful for all kinds of yarns. At least two patents were taken out, one in 1839 by J. Schofield and E. Leach,[11] and the other in 1854, 'an improvement', by A. Dobson.[12]

The Jute Industry

In Britain the jute industry is a relatively modern development. The machine processing of the fibres began even later than that of waste-silk spinning. In Bengal the spinning and weaving of jute had been carried out manually for many years. A limited amount of jute was also being imported into Britain in the early decades of the nineteenth century, most of it being wheel spun and hand woven in the carpet trade. Abingdon, in the county of Oxford, was the principal centre for this work. The fibres were also being used in other parts of the country for mixing with flax fibres in the spinning of the coarser kinds of linen yarns. The result was a very low-grade but cheaper product, and the practice was one which most flax spinners repudiated.

In 1838 the Dutch Government placed a large order with Dundee manufacturers for jute sacks, to be used to hold coffee beans in the coffee plantations in the West Indies. These sacks proved so successful for this purpose that they began to be used to contain other commodities, and the jute industry grew in importance in the Dundee district, where developments were now taking place leading to the use of more machines.[13]

Jute, like flax, is a bast fibre, forming the inner bark of the jute plant, and having long commercial fibres (up to about 15 ft [4·6 m] in length), made of cell fibres (up to about $\frac{1}{4}$ in [6·4 mm] long). The fibres also possess similar characteristics, such as low elasticity and

29 Noble's combing machine

30 The Northrop loom

31 Saltaire Mills

32 Manningham Mills

flexibility. It is, therefore, not surprising that the early attempts at spinning jute were made on flax machines. Even so, there are some pronounced differences between the two fibres, and it was soon discovered that modifications were needed in the flax machines. Thus, because jute fibres are coarser and harsher than flax, two carding machines in succession had to be used, and these were fitted with stronger teeth with the object of tearing the longer jute fibres into shorter lengths corresponding more nearly to those of the flax fibres. As was to be expected, some of the early adaptations of machines were not successful, but one important advance was made when softening processes were applied to the fibres, to reduce their harshness, and lubricants were added because of the absence of natural oils or waxes in the fibres. Another problem which was duly solved was that of constructing machines which would loosen and open out the very hard-pressed bales received from India. The gills on the drawing and roving frames were also specially designed for the coarser fibres. The spinning machines were based on the bobbin and flyer system as used in the flax industry, but made larger and stronger for the coarser fibres and yarns.

The industry developed more surely and more rapidly than happened in the early years of the other textile industries because it was possible to make use of the existing ideas and techniques already being applied in those industries, although it was not until 1855 that the first jute machinery was exported from Dundee to India, where the industry also began to develop.

CHAPTER TWENTY

Spinning: Further Developments

In the later years of the eighteenth and the early decades of the nineteenth centuries there seems to have been a slowing down in the rate of invention and development of spinning machines in Britain. It was as if the machinery-makers had decided they had reached a stage at which it was unlikely that newer methods of spinning would be forthcoming, and that concentration on developing and improving the existing methods was the policy to adopt. So improvements continued to be applied to the throstle frame and the mules apparently with little thought of any other ways of spinning which might be possible.

Certainly the initiative in this direction passed to America early in the nineteenth century. Samuel Slater, an apprentice at one of Strutt's mills, left England in 1789, taking with him sufficient information about machinery to enable him to begin cotton spinning there. By the turn of the century this industry was well established and inventors began to improve upon the existing machines and even to construct new types.

The least satisfactory feature of the throstle frame was the flyer. Compared with the plain spindle of the mule it was clumsy and obstructive; it had to be removed from the spindle and replaced each time the bobbins were changed; it consumed more power and was often distorted through careless handling, resulting in vibration and consequent excessive wear of spindle and bearing. These defects in turn restricted speeds and limited production. On the other hand, the throstle was a much simpler machine than the mule and could be tended by unskilled labour, mainly women and children, whereas the mule spinner had to be a trained and skilled operative. The problem requiring solution, therefore, was that of providing a simple, easily tended spinning machine without the use of flyers.

The Americans provided answers with two such machines. One

became known as the ring frame. Several inventors, working separately, seem to have contributed towards the introduction and development of the machine, all between 1829 and 1832. John Thorp of Providence, Rhode Island, was one of these. He took out a patent in the United States in 1828, and this was protected in Britain in 1829.[1] Instead of a flyer, he used a hook 'which I cause to revolve round or with a circular rim or hoop'. Both ideas are shown in drawings, one illustrating a hook travelling around the rim of the hoop, the other showing a hook fixed to the hoop, which is itself rotated. As will be seen, the former provides the fundamental principle on which the ring frame was based.

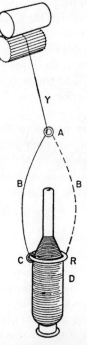

Figure 64   Ring spinning, twisting and winding units

Other American patentees were Addison and Stevens, who applied jointly and who appear to have been the first to use the term 'traveller', Sharp in 1831, and Jencks in 1832.

At least one reliable authority believed that Jencks was the true inventor of the ring frame.[2]

Fig. 64 shows a perspective view of the twisting and winding units

of a ring frame. The name is, of course, taken from the ring R which
surrounds the bobbin D and its spindle. Moving freely round a flange
on the ring R is a small C-shaped piece of steel wire termed a
traveller (C). The yarn Y from the drawing rollers passes down
through a guide A situated directly above the spindle, thence through
the traveller and on to the bobbin. As the bobbin rotates, the yarn is
whirled round it, carrying the traveller round the ring as it 'bal-
loons' through centrifugal force between traveller and yarn guide,
so twisting the yarn. But as the rollers deliver more yarn, so the
traveller loses speed and yarn is wound on the bobbin. The traveller
thus replaced the cumbersome flyer and much higher speeds and
smoother running resulted. The ring was made to move slowly up
and down to distribute the yarn along the bobbin.

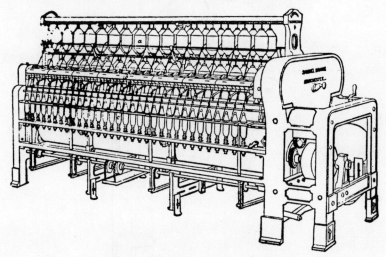

Figure 65   Ring spinning frame

Although the machine was introduced into Britain a few years
after its invention, it was not considered satisfactory at the time. Certainly there were early defects and difficulties, but the Americans set
to work to rectify these and in a few years the machine had largely
replaced the throstle frame. In Britain it did not become established
in the cotton industry until some fifty years later.[3] In the wool industries it did not prove so successful. Fig. 65 shows a general view
and shortened version of an early ring frame.

The other spinning machine referred to earlier was the invention of C. Danforth, patented in the United States in 1828 and in Britain, under the name of Hutchison, in 1829.[4] J. Thorp patented a similar machine later in 1828 and called it a 'can spinner'. For some years Danforth's machine was known as Danforth's throstle frame, but it is now generally known as the cap frame. Fig. 66, a side section, shows the essential spinning and winding elements. The spindle, which does not rotate, was fitted with a 'cape' or 'cap' E. A tube shown by broken lines within the bobbin D was rotated through the

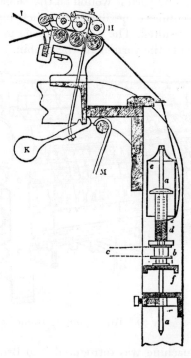

Figure 66   Cap spinning frame, sectional elevation

band C and pulley B, carrying the bobbin with it. The yarn, having passed from the drawing rollers above, was taken under the lower edge of the cap and on to the bobbin. But this bobbin rotation also took the yarn round with it, causing the length of yarn between bobbin and rollers to be twisted. Friction between yarn and cap edge, aided by air resistance against the ballooning yarn above, retarded the yarn rotation to some degree, so that as the yarn was emerging from the rollers it was being wound on the bobbin as well as being twisted. An up and down traverse of the bobbin caused the yarn to be distributed along the length of the bobbin.

Because the spindle was stationary, the machine was sometimes referred to as the dead-spindle machine. Relatively simple, it was introduced into the Yorkshire worsted industry in 1831, but, for some reason, it was not a success.[5] During the 1850s it was again tried, and proved very successful, especially in the Bradford worsted-spinning industry.[6] The machine is now largely used in the worsted-spinning industries throughout the world, although it did not prove satisfactory for cotton spinning.

Preparatory Processes

In Britain, during the early part of the nineteenth century, inventors were engaged in trying to solve the problem of providing a satisfactory machine or machines which would operate between the drawing frame and the spinning machine, especially in the processing of cotton. The difficulties to be overcome have been indicated in Chapter 8, where several attempts by Arkwright and his associates are described. The flyer and bobbin system of twisting and winding was ultimately adopted as likely to give the best results, using, of course, much larger flyers and bobbins than were used in the throstle frame to accommodate the thicker material. One important change was the provision of a hollow leg in the flyer, within which the softer slubbings or rovings could be protected from air resistance.

But it was the winding problem which proved the most difficult to solve. The slubbings were too weak to pull the bobbins round, and so both flyers and bobbins had to be driven by belts or geared wheels. But as the bobbins filled, so the peripheral speed of the surface on which the slubbings were to be wound increased, and it was necessary to provide means for varying the bobbin speeds accordingly. At first a long conical drum was used, which was caused to move laterally (the belt remaining in one position) to provide this speed variation. Later two conical complementary drums were used, and the belt was made to move at intervals along them as the bobbins increased in diameter. Even this method presented difficulties, one of which was the slipping of the cone belt drive because of the excessive power which had to be transmitted to drive the bobbins, a factor which resulted in uneven winding and defective rovings.

The solution to this problem came with the introduction of a differential drive, which became known as a 'sun and planet' motion. It combined the direct-gearing drive from the main shaft of the machine with that from the cone-drum drive, so that the latter only provided the *difference* between flyer and bobbin speeds, i.e. the winding speeds, so taking most of the transmission power away from the belt. It was patented by H. Houldsworth of Manchester in 1826,[7] and was based on a device patented by J. Green of Mansfield in 1823.[8] The principle is also believed to have been applied in America in 1822, by A. Arnold. Thus success was finally achieved, and the machine became known as a flyframe.

While inventors in Britain were engaged on this machine, C. Danforth in America was working on a simpler machine for the same purpose.

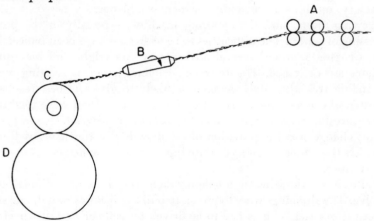

Figure 67   Diagram showing principle of the tube frame

It was patented in Britain under the name of Dyer in 1825[9] and became known as the tube frame. The strand of fibres, after being drawn in the usual manner by the drawing rollers A (Fig. 67), passed through a rapidly rotating small tube B before being wound on the bobbin C driven by contact with the drum D. Obviously there was no winding problem here, since the peripheral speed of the bobbin was constant. But this middle twisting was temporary or false (several instances of this false twisting have been mentioned in earlier chapters), since the length of roving between A and B would be twisted in one direction while that between B and C would be twisted an equal amount in the opposite direction. So the roving would be practically untwisted as it reached the bobbin and would be weak and unstable, stretching unevenly and often breaking as it unwound at the next process. But the frame was used for some years because of its simple construction compared with the flyer-type machines. However, the application of the differential motion to the latter (it was patented a year after Dyer's patent) ultimately led to the tube frames being replaced by flyframes.

In the worsted industry bobbin and flyer machines were also used, and because the longer fibres gave stronger rovings it was generally possible for the rovings to pull the bobbins round, as in the throstle frame, without recourse to a separate bobbin drive. No winding problem was therefore involved. But when finer yarns and therefore finer rovings were produced, the latter were often found to be too weak to turn the bobbins. To overcome this difficulty the worsted spinners began to use roving frames of the type being used in the cotton industry, complete with cone-drum driving and differential motion. This occurred in the 1890s and the process became known as 'cone drawing', as distinct from the 'open drawing' normally used.

Yarn-winding Processes

The process of winding transfers yarns from one form of package to another and was originally carried out as a convenience and an aid to efficient operation. Later it served also as a means for cleaning yarns and removing some kinds of imperfection. It was a process which began to be carried out in spinning mills, obviating the transport of bobbins to weaving and knitting mills and the return of empty bobbins to the spinning mills. This need did not arise in mule spinning mills, since the 'cops' did not have a central core or support. Yarns were often 'reeled' into skeins at the spinning mills, especially when they had to be wet processed (e.g. bleached or dyed). With the increasing use of ring spinning frames, warp yarns began to be wound on beams at the spinning mill for transport to weaving centres. For the knitting industry the most suitable package for feeding to the knitting machine was generally one from which the yarn could be withdrawn over one end, while the package remained stationary. Winding machines were constructed which produced bottle-shaped bobbins for this purpose—when filled they were shaped like sloping-shouldered bottles over the 'neck' of which the yarns were readily withdrawn. The winding took place at the knitting factory.

At least three important stages of development in winding took place during the nineteenth century. First during the 1860s came the invention of the quick-traverse machine, which by causing the yarn to traverse rapidly across the package built up a cylinder of yarn without supporting flanges; in fact, the yarn could be wound on paper tubes instead of heavy wood bobbins. A few years later a machine was devised which wound cone-shaped packages—a package from which yarn could be withdrawn over the small end of the cone, displacing the clumsy bottle-bobbin. The third step was the invention of the precision winding machine in 1892, by means of which yarns could be wound in evenly and usually closely spaced coils throughout the package, resulting in a compact structure holding much more yarn.[10] The outcome of these developments was the transfer of more of the winding processes to the spinning mills, especially of knitting or hosiery yarns.

An invention of particular interest to the sewing-thread industry was that of William Weild, of Manchester, who in 1858[11] patented a machine which wound spools on reels of cotton thread, and after improvements a few years later automatically stopped the winding when a predetermined length had been wound on the reels, cut the threads, fastened the cut threads into the flanges of the reels, removed the reels, replaced them with empty ones and started winding again.[12] The timing of the invention was also appropriate, for sewing machines, following improvements introduced by several inventors, were soon to become more widely used both in factories and in homes.

CHAPTER TWENTY-ONE

Roberts' Automatic Mule

A machine which came into use in the early days of mule spinning was the stretching frame or stretching mule. It was based on the action of the mule; in fact, it could be described as a mule without drawing rollers, only one pair of rollers being used to deliver the yarn to the spindles. It was used in the fine spinning mills, giving the rovings a final stretching and soft twisting before being taken to the mule.

Early improvements applied to the mule resulted in parts of the machine being driven by steam power; these included the drawing rollers, the spindles during twisting and the carriage on its outward run. But for the inward run the mule 'minder' took over to wind the yarn on the cop. It was a delicate operation requiring considerable skill and judgement, since he had to maintain a careful relationship between the speed at which the carriage moved inwards and the peripheral speed of the cop at the position on the conical end to which the yarn was being guided. Failure to maintain the correct relationship resulted either in the yarns all breaking or, if his spindle speed was too low, in a slackening of tensions which could cause twisted and tangled yarns.

These were the operations which Roberts was asked to make automatic, or, to use the more common expression at the time, 'self-acting'.[1]

The main problems which Roberts faced may be stated briefly by reference to the manner in which a mule cop is built up. Fig. 68 shows a partly formed cop, the left side in section, where the diagonal lines represent layers of wound yarn. A, B, C, and D are thickened lines to show how these layers change in length as the cop is being formed. The first layer wound on the spindle at A is relatively short and subsequent layers are longer, reaching their maximum length at C. Thereafter the length remains constant, being the same at D.

173

This early lengthening, associated with the starting positions at the bottom of each layer, gradually forms a conical surface on the cop and a rounded base.

The outer view of the cop on the right of the illustration shows two spirals of yarn on the conical end, one a fine-pitched spiral, the

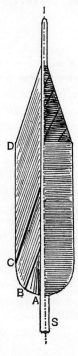

Figure 68   Construction of a mule cop

other coarse pitched, the purpose of the latter being to prevent the embedding of the fine-pitched spirals into each other. To guide the yarn on to the cop by mechanisms was a relatively easy matter, and this was accomplished in a manner shown by the diagram Fig. 69. The winding faller wire N is attached to levers L and P (fulcrum at F) and P in turn is attached to the rod X. The parts so far indicated are all mounted on the carriage (they should be compared with those having the same reference letters in Fig. 29). A small roller or bowl on the lower end of the rod X rests on a rail Z, and it can be seen that the bowl will run along this rail as the carriage moves in, causing the wire N to move quickly downwards, resulting in a coarse spiral of wound yarn on the cop, and then to move slowly upwards to give the fine spiral. The 'copping rail', as it came to be known, rests on the inclines W, W_1, and after each run-in of the carriage these inclines moved a little in the direction shown by the arrows, causing the rail to drop slightly so that the next layer of yarn was wound a little higher on the cop.

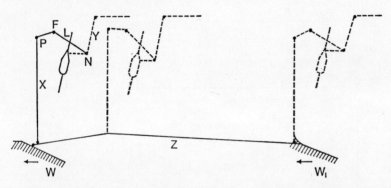

Figure 69   Diagram showing how the yarn is guided on to the cop

Much more difficult to solve was the problem of providing the correct winding speeds for the spindles. These speeds may be classified as follows:

(*a*) A variable spindle speed because the carriage speed varies, starting and finishing slowly.

(*b*) A high and practically constant spindle speed (except for the factors mentioned under (*a*)) when the first few layers are being wound, i.e. at position A, Fig. 68.

(*c*) A progressive slowing down of this speed as the cop bottom is forming, but reaching the same high speed as winding reaches the top of the cone positions A to C.

(*d*) The same speed variation for each layer during the building of the body of the cop, positions C to E.

The fundamental principles on which Robert's solution to these problems was based may also be explained by a diagram. Assume a chain is attached to and coiled round a drum at A (Fig. 70) and the other end to a fixed point X. If now the drum is conveyed from A to

B as shown at I, it will rotate and unwind a length of the cord equal to the distance moved. But if the point X also moves in the direction of the drum, the length unwound will be equal to the distance moved by the drum less the distance moved horizontally by X. If X is attached to an arm or lever at X^1, and this lever turns as shown in II to position X^2, a variable speed of drum will result, beginning

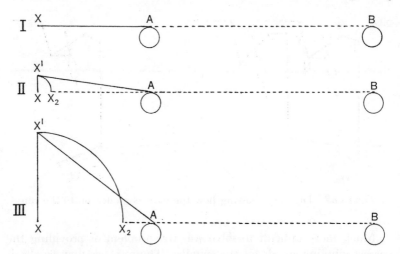

Figure 70   Diagram illustrating principle of mule quadrant

slowly and accelerating as the movement of X^1 approaches a vertical direction. If the radius of this arc of movement is increased, as shown at III the speed becomes more variable because there is a greater horizontal movement of X^1, although towards the end, i.e. nearing X^2, the almost vertical movement results in practically the same terminal speed of drum as in II.

By gearing the drum to the cylinder driving the spindles and attaching the end X (Fig. 70) to a nut on a screw in the arm D of the quadrant A (Fig. 71), the spindle speeds required can be obtained. The quick downward movement of the winding faller wire to produce the coarse-pitched spiral does not present a winding problem and may be ignored, the arm D being set to attain its vertical position as the winding of the fine spiral begins. The cog wheel B driving the quadrant is turned through a band attached to the carriage. The chain is shown at F and in two other positions. The

drive from the chain drum H on the carriage G to the 'wharf' or
pulley T on the spindle is also shown.

Reverting to the speed requirements above, these were obtained
as follows:

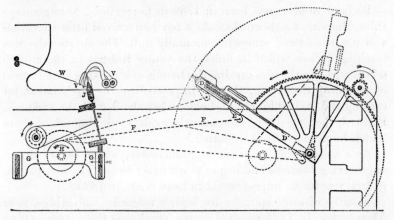

Figure 71   The mule quadrant

(*a*) The quadrant was operated from the movement of the
carriage and therefore its speed varied with that of the
carriage.

(*b*) At the beginning of spinning a new set of cops the mule
minder turns the screw in the quadrant arm to bring the nut
to its lowest position. This provides the practically constant
spindle speed required.

(*c*) At each inward run of the carriage the screw is turned automatically, so raising the nut a short distance, providing progressively slower starting speeds, but finishing with the same
high speeds.

(*d*) When the cop bottom has been formed the screw ceases to
turn and the same speed variation then continues as the
body of the cop is formed.

The invention was a remarkable achievement by a very clever
and inventive engineer, and soon the self-acting mule came into
extensive use.[2] The mule minder no longer needed to be so highly
skilled, although he still had to be much more skilful and experienced than most other textile workers. Plate 27 shows part of a mule

room in the early decades of the nineteenth century, i.e. before
Roberts' invention, since no quadrants are to be seen. The machines
were arranged in pairs facing each other so that one 'minder' with
assistants ('piecers') could more easily tend them.

Richard Roberts was born in 1789 in Correghofa, Montgomery-
shire, the son of a shoemaker. As a boy he received little education
and was considered somewhat mentally dull. The curate who was
teaching a class which included the young Roberts in the church
school once caught him carving the handle of a walking stick instead
of attending the lesson. He was impressed by the boy's talent for
carving and invited him to his home, where he had a lathe and tools.
Richard, then aged ten, subsequently made a spinning wheel there
which he presented to his mother.[3]

As a young man he went to Manchester, where he set up an
engineering business and began to construct looms. His first patent,
in fact, was for an improvement in loom reeds, in 1822.[4]

A strike of mule spinners for higher wages in Stalybridge, near
Manchester, in 1824 resulted in the employers there approaching
leading engineers in the district to ask for a self-acting mule, so that
less-skilled men could be employed and the strike broken. But, like
the experts who told Cartwright that a power-driven loom was an
impossibility, so now the spinning employers were given similar
answers regarding an automatic mule. They persisted in their
inquiries, however, and saw Roberts, who informed them that he
knew nothing about mules (as Cartwright had known nothing
about looms) and would not commit himself. Under further pressure,
and being given the opportunity of studying a mule installed in his
own workshop, he set himself the task, and by 1825 had taken out
his first patent, which appears to include the 'copping rail'.[5] Five
years later he took out his second patent, in which the quadrant or
'radial arm' is specified;[6] together they resulted in the fully automatic or self-acting mule.

Roberts took out many other successful inventions, both in textile
and in general engineering and became one of Manchester's most
famous engineers.[7]

He died in 1864, and in spite of his successes in the field of
mechanical invention, in his later years he lived in a condition of
comparative poverty.

CHAPTER TWENTY-TWO

Knitting: Further Developments

Additions to and modifications of the combined Lee and Strutt inventions were made in later years, chiefly resulting in more ornamental hose and knitted fabrics, often with holes or eyelets, which give a more lace-like appearance to the fabrics. These effects were obtained by the use of a number of fine projections or 'points' which were made to descend as required on to the needles, lifting off the stitches and transferring them to adjacent needles, either to the right or left, so leaving a space or hole in the fabric.

A more fundamental development took place about 1775, when the first warp knitting machine was made. Previously, all the machine knitting had been of the kind now termed weft knitting, i.e. the yarn passed across the width of the fabric, each row being interlooped with the adjacent row, the yarn lying generally in the same direction as the weft in a woven cloth. In the new machine a warp was introduced—a series of threads which had been previously wound on a large roller, similar to the warp beam for a loom. This was placed at the back of the knitting frame and the threads passed through eyelets in individual guides. These guides were moved in conjunction with the orthodox needles so that each thread formed its own interloops, much as a schoolboy interloops a length of string. In addition, however, the threads were looped with adjacent threads by side movements of the guides. The two sets of loopings thus produced a knitted fabric. It is not known definitely who invented the process; it has been attributed to J. Crane and also to J. Tarratt, both of Nottinghamshire.[1]

The machine created a breakthrough in knitted productions. The fabrics were not so elastic as those made on the stocking frame, in this sense resembling woven fabrics which they sometimes replaced, and cotton fabrics knitted on the machine were cut into shapes and sewn up as garments. Warp knitting later grew into an important

179

section of the knitting industry, the machines being developed to produce many lace-like fabrics as well as closely knit underwear fabrics.

Another important invention was that of William Dawson, a Leicester framework knitter, in 1791.[2] He applied a notched wheel or cam to warp knitting machines, a device which acted as a selecting medium for the production of knitted patterns—a process previously carried out manually by the knitter. It became known as the Dawson wheel and has since been applied to many other kinds of machines. It has been likened to the catches of the barrel of an organ used for the opening and closing of the pipes,[3] a method which had been in use some ten years before Dawson's patent. (A similar comparison was made when a dobby was devised in 1817 for the loom.) The invention also led to the power driving of knitting machines.

The circular knitting machine, which produced fabrics in tubular form, is usually stated to be the invention of M. I. Brunel, the famous engineer and father of a still more famous son. He applied for and obtained a patent in 1816,[4] but in his application he stated that it was a 'communication', implying that he was not the true inventor. He called the machine the tricoteur. He used Lee's method of knitting, with bearded needles, sinkers and pressers, although owing to the circular arrangement of these parts he used different mechanisms to operate them. For a number of years the machine was not taken up to any extent by the knitting industry, which was obsessed with the production of stockings; tubular fabrics being the same diameter throughout would be unsuitable for this purpose, and if they were cut to shape and sewn would depreciate the standards of the trade. Framework knitters, too, thought the use of the machine would lead to unemployment.

In 1847, M. Townsend, a framework knitter of Nottingham, added mechanism which produced rib-knitting on circular machines.[5] This development led to the circular machine coming into general use, especially for stockings, since the rib stitch gave so much more elasticity to the stockings that the uniform character of the tubular fabric was no longer a disadvantage. In 1855, A. Paget, of Loughborough, made a circular knitting machine which could be power driven. It included 'an arrangement . . . for driving the machine by an endless belt or band, the slackening of which suspends the motion of the machine'.[6]

A year later Townsend took out a patent which has had a tre-
mendous influence on the knitting industry.[7] This was a hooked
needle, similar in general appearance to the bearded needle, but
having a hinged attachment to open and close the hook as shown in
Fig. 72. At first termed the tumbler needle, it is now generally

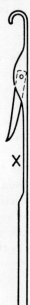

Figure 72   The latch needle

known as the latch needle. When working in a vertical position the
latch normally hung down, with the hook open. As the needle
descended the yarn lying along the stem at about position X lifted
the latch shown and so closed the hook. When the yarn had passed
over the top of the needle the latch fell by gravity to leave the hook
open. Obviously the presser was not needed to close the hook, and to
this extent the mechanism of the machine was simplified. One disadvantage was and is that a relatively substantial thickness of needle
was required to accommodate the hinge. So for fine-gauge work it
was still necessary to use the bearded needle.

An important development in the non-circular knitting machine
was that of William Cotton, of Loughborough. The invention was a

development of earlier machines dating from 1769, which all operated on the lines of the stocking frame. He took out patents in 1851, 1860, and 1863.[8] Included in them was the automatic widening and narrowing of the fabric on power-driven machines. Gradually the machine, which is still known as 'Cotton's patent', was developed until it became fully automatic in action, and many more variations in patterning were devised, including the application of Jacquard's system of punched cards.

Developments also continued in the other types of knitting machines, all based on the fundamental inventions outlined. The power driving of the earlier knitting machines was adopted later than it had been in the spinning and weaving industries, although as long ago as 1816 John Heathcoat had applied rotary motions to the stocking frame, 'causing the machine to work entirely by the revolution of one pulley or drum'.[9]

Although the nineteenth century saw some of the basic inventions from which modern knitting machines have been developed, there was for a period a slowing down of really effective progress towards greater technical achievements. In fact, it was not until after the Second World War that developments took place which have brought the industry to its present important place in the world of textiles.

CHAPTER TWENTY-THREE

Combing

The combing of textile fibres should not be confused with the carding operation. The latter is largely a surface action, i.e. the wire teeth form areas of points so close together that most of the fibres remain on the surface.

In combing, one or more rows of teeth move *through* the fibres, exactly as in the combing of hair. The results of these operations also differ. After carding, short fibres such as those of cotton, for example, are left in a generally criss-cross condition, but the hand carding of the longer wool and flax fibres leaves them in a straighter condition and in a roughly parallel order, although many wools still retain much of their natural waviness. After combing, all fibres tend to lie in an approximately parallel formation, and some natural waviness has been removed. Combing also acts as a more effective cleanser and removes many of the shorter fibres.

For centuries combing was done by hand operations in which a few implements were used. Wool and waste silks were prepared for spinning by these methods, and since some of the early combing machines used in the worsted industry were based on hand-combing techniques it will be of interest to consider how the operation was carried out. No clear detailed description by a hand comber, of the manner in which he operated, appears to be available. Some writers have attempted to describe the processes and in one case at least the description was based on the oral account of a one-time hand comber, but told many years after he had left the occupation. The various accounts differ, whether because of faulty understanding or because combers in different districts adopted different techniques, it is difficult to say. For these reasons, the following description of hand combing is general rather than detailed, but should serve as an introduction to a consideration of mechanical combing.

Two combs were used, each with steel teeth tapering from base to point and several inches long, closely set in wood blocks to which handles were attached. There were several rows of these teeth; in fact, the 'combs' were more like coarse brushes with steel bristles. Because heated teeth combed the wool more effectively with fewer breakages of fibres, the combs were kept hot by frequent heating over a stove. One comb was fixed to an upright, with the teeth vertical, and the wool, which had previously been washed and wrung out between rollers, was sprinkled with oil, taken by hand in small quantities and thrown or 'lashed on' the teeth of the fixed comb, leaving a fringe hanging from the edges.

With the fixed comb now placed with the teeth horizontal the free comb was taken by the comber and brought down with a semi-circular motion into the fringe, beginning at the extreme edges. The action was repeated many times, the strokes going gradually deeper into the fringe until the free comb had collected most of the wool from the fixed comb. The combs were then changed over and the actions repeated until the wool was again collected on what was now the free comb. The process was termed 'jigging', being, in fact, a preliminary or first combing. The wool was later given a second combing, using a similar technique; the combed tufts were then collected and joined to form slivers or 'tops' for the worsted spinner. Short fibres in the wool became embedded in the combs and these (termed 'noils') were removed and sold to woollen spinners.

Two important factors to be noted in these hand-combing operations which influenced the early invention of combing machines were (a) the lashing-on action, to ensure that the fibres were well embedded between the comb teeth, and (b) the graduated combing, i.e. combing which began at the extreme ends of the fringe and gradually extended further into it, obviously to avoid damaging the tangled fibres.

The wool comber's work was arduous, yet it was one which required experience and skill, and during the period when processes preceding and following that of combing began to be done by machinery the men were in a strong bargaining position for higher wages. In time their demands were considered by employers to have become excessive. They often rejected these demands and strikes and disorders took place in many districts.

As was to be expected, the employers began to seek for a means of combing by machinery. Immediately before 1790 a particularly

severe turn-out, as the strikes were called, took place, requiring the
action of magistrates to quell the disorders in Halifax, and it is
significant that in that year and again in 1792 Edmund Cartwright,
better known for his invention of the power loom, took out patents
for a wool-combing machine.[1]

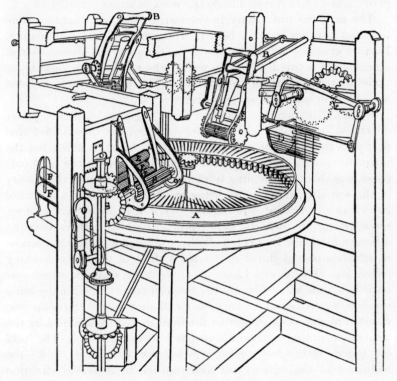

Figure 73   Cartwright's combing machine

Fig. 73 shows a perspective view of the machine, the main feature
of which was a circular rotating frame A, 5–6 ft (1·5–1·8 m) in
diameter and fitted with radial comb teeth projecting inwards as
shown. The wool was fed to these teeth by the rollers C, mounted on
a frame B. At intervals this frame was raised and then brought
down quickly to impale the wool projecting from the rollers on to
the radial comb. Here can be seen Cartwright's mechanical imitation of the 'slashing-on' action of the hand comber—in fact, the

mechanism B was known as the crank-slasher. The long fibres held by the radial comb were removed as they passed by the rollers E, and the shorter ones by the smaller rotating combs D. The combs were heated during the operation by a stove placed underneath the circular frame. The machine was nicknamed Big Ben (after a local prize-fighter) and was said to do the work of twenty men.

The machine was relatively successful, for more machines were installed in other factories both in Yorkshire and in Leicestershire. Further evidence of their success at the time was the presentation of a number of petitions to Parliament by the hand combers asking for their use to be restricted or prohibited. The petitions were rejected and the men became less aggressive.[2]

Perhaps the success or failure of these 'Big Bens' depended partly on the skills with which they were worked and maintained and partly on the classes of wool being combed. Accounts differ, but the ultimate verdict, since judgement must be based on the final outcome, was that the machines were a comparative failure, the quality of the combing, it was said, being much below that of the skilled hand comber. A number of attempts were made by other inventors, some trying to improve Cartwright's machine, others devising different methods. In 1814, J. Collier patented a combing machine in which a pair of fluted rollers fed a sheet of wool to a combing roller, and Dawson and Lister also invented a machine which was tried by a number of firms as the lesser of two evils, since the hand combers again began to bargain for higher wages. Striking was resorted to and one turn-out in Bradford in 1825 was joined by the weavers, resulting in the mill-owners closing their mills. The lock-out lasted twenty-two weeks, a period which not only broke the resistance of the strikers but also resulted in increased attention being given to the question of mechanical combing. In the meantime most firms continued to employ hand combers and, no doubt, the latter began to feel their jobs were secure, and combing by machine just a dream. In 1832 they turned out once more, this time at a factory near Lancaster, whence it spread to Bradford and Leeds.

But it proved to be their last strike. J. Platt, in a communication from abroad, had taken out a patent[3] in 1827 for a combing machine which gave better results than earlier machines. It consisted essentially of two large circular combs, D, D, shown in perspective in the left hand drawing of Fig. 74. They operated in different planes, as shown clearly in the right hand drawing, which is a side elevation, so that the comb teeth opposed each other at an angle. The wool was fed to one of the circles, and the two circles, whilst revolving, were brought closer together. By this means a gradual penetration by the combs into the wool took place, along with a transfer of the fibres to

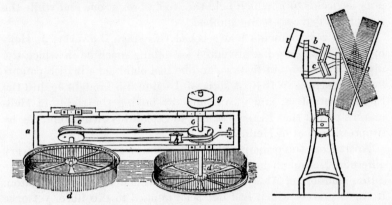

Figure 74   Platt's combing machine

the second circle. When the combing was completed the rotation of the combs was reversed and the longer fibres removed by rollers. The short fibres which remained embedded in the comb teeth were removed by hand.

Improved machines of this type were in operation in 1835:

Large machines are now at work in Leeds. In one of them the comb-wheels are ten feet in diameter and are furnished with hollow spikes filled with steam which keeps the whole apparatus at a proper combing heat. These wheels are made to revolve slowly while a boy, seated on the ground, dresses one of them with wool. They are then made to revolve with great rapidity . . . during which revolutions they gradually approach each other.[4]

It appears to have been the first of the combing machines to comb wool between two adjacent circular combs, and according to James it was still in use when his book was published in 1857.

Several other inventions were patented during the period which followed. One of these was that of G. E. Donisthorpe, of Leeds, who obtained patents[5] in 1842 and 1843. These drew the attention of

S. C. Lister (later Lord Masham—see Chapter 25). They joined
forces and a combing machine was devised which soon proved to be
superior to all the earlier machines. Patents were taken out in 1849,
1850, 1851, and 1852[6] (the last two in Lister's name only). One of
the important features of these patents was the provision of a gripping device or 'nip' which held the wool fibres at one end while the
rest of the tuft was being combed.

Before developments had reached this stage, however, J. Heilmann of Mulhouse had invented a combing machine in which the
nip was an important feature, and he had obtained a British patent[7]
for this machine in 1846. A successful action was brought against the
English patentees, and it was only by buying the rights of Heilmann's patent that Lister was able to exploit his own patent, i.e. by
suppressing that of Heilmann.

Apart from the principle of nipping, the two machines were very
different. Heilmann had been awarded 5,000 francs offered by the
cotton spinners of Alsace for a machine which would comb cotton.
It was a process which had not been applied to this fibre, yet once
established, it enabled spinners to spin finer, smoother, and more
lustrous yarns. The machine also proved readily adaptable for wool
combing and continued in use for both purposes for many years.
Cotton spinners in Lancashire paid £30,000 for the cotton-combing
rights, and a Leeds engineering firm paid £20,000 in 1890 to use it
for the combing of flax.[8] It was used on the Continent for combing
silk as well as flax, wool, and cotton.

Fig. 75 shows a sectional side elevation of the essential features
of the machine as used for combing cotton, in four stages of the cycle
of operations. A cylinder carries a comb segment B and a grooved
or fluted segment C. At stage 1 the feed rollers F have fed a short
length of cotton in sheet form (about 12 in wide) which is held by
the nippers G and H and combing is beginning. At 2 the combing is
finishing and at 3 the 'detaching roller' E has descended on to the
fluted segment, gripping the combed tuft and detaching it from the
uncombed fibres, an operation assisted by the comb T, which has
also descended so that the rear part of the detached tuft is also
combed. The 'attaching rollers' D have also reversed to bring a little
of the previously combed material back. At 4 both the detaching and
attaching operations are shown completed, the roller E having laid
the newly combed fibres on the portion turned back by the rollers

COMBING   189

D, D. The nippers have also opened to receive a further length of
cotton fed forward by the rollers F, F. A rotating brush (not shown)
below the cylinder removes the short fibres and impurities retained
by the combs. The machine was constructed with a number of
'units' or 'heads' in a line as shown in Plate 28.

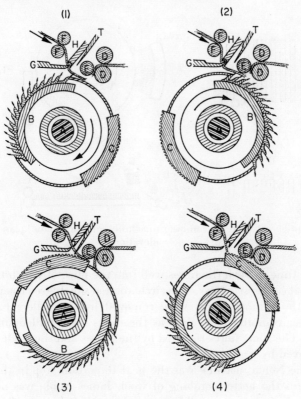

Figure 75   Sectional elevations of the combing units in Heilmann's
cotton combing machine

The Donisthorpe and Lister combing machine, after a number of
improvements, became known as the Lister comb, the essential
features of which are shown in Fig. 76. The wool passed through the
feed rollers A to the gills or fallers B, moving from A to C at a higher
speed than the rate of delivery by the feed rollers and so straightening and combing the fibres in the same way that fallers operated

between drawing rollers. But instead of a second pair of rollers, a nipping device C held the fibres and took them to position C1, giving them a further combing. The nippers now released the fibres, allowing the comb D to take them to position D1, and to lay them on heated pins or teeth in the comb circle E. A brush G descended at the

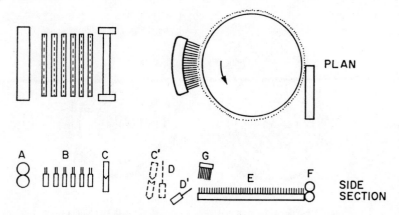

Figure 76   Lister's combing machine, diagrammatic plan and side elevation

same time to push the fibres well into the pins, of which there were several concentric rows. The circle rotated slowly (see the plan view) and the combed fibres were removed by the rollers F, where a further combing took place as the fibres were pulled through the pins. The short fibres retained by the fallers and the circle pins were removed by brushes.

The Noble machine was the next important step in the progress towards the better combing of wool. James Noble was nearly fifty before he invented a really successful combing machine. But for many of those fifty years he had experimented with combing machines, and had taken out a number of patents. It was in 1853, however, that he patented the machine with which his name is associated,[9] and in Britain the Noble comb is now the machine mostly used for the combing of wool. Again a large horizontal circle was a central feature, but the method of combing differed considerably from that of the Lister machine. A diagrammatic plan, Fig. 77, shows one large circle A, and two smaller ones B, B, all fitted with vertical

pins which were heated. (Originally only one of the smaller circles
was used, but the second was added a few years later.) It will be seen
by reference to the arrows that all three circles turned in the same
direction; they also moved at the same circumferential speeds.

The wool fibres were fed to the large circle and as they reached

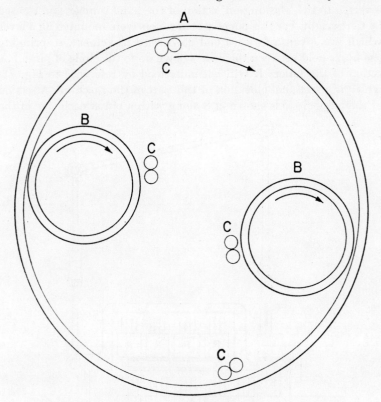

Figure 77   Noble's combing machine, diagrammatic plan

the places where they were nearest the small circles they became
straddled across both sets of pins. But because the speeds were the
same at these places, combing did not take place until the spaces
between the large and small circles began to widen. After this combing, the fibres were removed from the pins by vertically placed
rollers C. The general appearance of a Noble comb may be seen in
Plate 29.

Another combing machine invented in the 1850s was the Holden or 'square-motion' comb. It was the invention of Isaac Holden, who patented it in 1856.[10] Again a large horizontal circle of pins was used, but these pins served only to hold the fibres while the combing was carried out mainly by the use of gills or fallers. Holden also reverted to the 'slashing-on' action of the hand comber and as used by Cartwright. For this purpose feed rollers were mounted on a lever which was given a forward and downward movement, so bringing the fibres held between the rollers down on to the circle of pins. The action of the fallers R will be understood by reference to Fig. 78, which is a sectional elevation of this part of the machine. A section of the large circle is shown at S along with a pin at each side of the

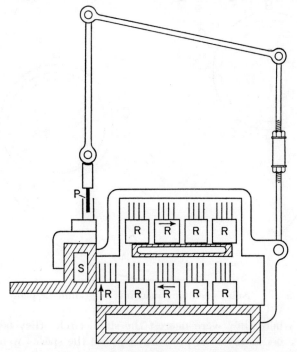

Figure 78   Holden's combing machine, part side section

plate P, whose function was to press the fibres down between pins. As each faller rose close to the circle S its pins penetrated the fringe of fibres projecting from the circle pins. It then moved to the right, so combing the fringe until it reached the other end, when it was dropped into the lower row to be cleaned and moved towards the circle again. (Whence the term 'square-motion', which Lister had used in 1846.) Each succeeding faller moved in the same path, but instead of screws, levers and cams were used to actuate them. As these operations proceeded so the large circle moved round to receive more fibres and to bring them into position for combing.

The combing machines mentioned in this chapter have been described in as simple a manner as possible by restricting the descriptions to the parts which actually process the fibres, and showing these in diagram form. The machines are too complicated mechanically for detailed explanation in a work of this kind, but it is hoped that the general reader has obtained a fair idea of their *combing* actions. Those who desire more information on the history of these machines are referred to the work by James Burnley.[11]

CHAPTER TWENTY-FOUR

Weaving: Further Developments

Preparing for Weaving

It will be appropriate to consider some of the developments in the preparation of yarns for weaving before describing more loom improvements.

The yarns which are to form the warp need much more preparation after spinning than do the weft yarns. The balling and chaining of yarns described earlier was in due course done by machines. J. Taylor and R. Hurst invented a balling machine in 1850[1] and W. Hurst the chain or linking machine in 1883.[2] Dressing was later largely discarded in the cotton industry in favour of 'sizing', although it was retained in the flax and jute industries. In the cotton industry the term 'dressing' began to be restricted to the transferring of the ball or chain warp to the beam, without the application of any paste or size. The tape-sizing machine was invented by W. H. Hornby and W. Kenworthy, of Blackburn, Lancashire, in 1839.[3] The term tape was used because in this machine the yarns were first laid side by side, forming a series of flat, tape-like groups of threads.[4] The most important result of using the machine was that the yarns were saturated with the size, and not merely given a surface coating. This result was obtained by immersing the yarn in a boiling mixture, and squeezing out excess size between rollers. They were then dried by passing them over the surfaces of large, steam-heated cylinders.

In 1852,[5] J. Bullough and others patented some improvements in the machine which accelerated the changing of the supply beams. It now became known as the slasher sizing machine and later the terms tape and slasher became synonymous.[6]

Mule-spun weft cops were used in the loom—they could be readily 'skewered' on to the shuttle tongue. Yarns were also later spun on small bobbins (weft pirns) on the ring frame and these, too, were used in the shuttle. But there were many instances where it became

195

necessary to wind yarns specially for use in the shuttle—e.g. where
the spun yarns had first to be skeined for bleaching or dyeing. This
weft-winding process presented an early problem to the machinery-
makers owing to the varying diameters of the conical surface on
which the yarns had to be wound if they were to be unwound over
the end of the pirn in the shuttle. In 1857, Willis and Chell[7]
patented a machine in which a uniform winding speed was maintained by providing an appropriate variable-speed drive to the pirns;
it was a machine which came into extensive use.

Power Loom Improvements

William Horrocks, of Stockport, introduced a number of improvements in a loom he patented in 1803,[8] and this loom set the pace for
the growth, which soon became rapid, in the use of the power loom.
Indeed, it has been said that in the first decade of the nineteenth

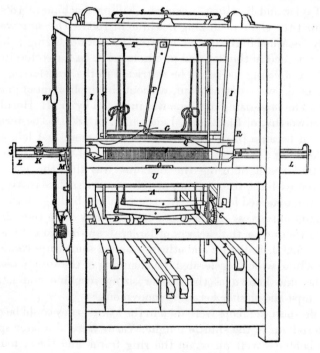

Figure 79 Horrocks' power loom

century Johnson, Radcliffe, and Horrocks did for power weaving what Arkwright did for spinning. One feature of the loom was a crankshaft to move the slay, instead of the eccentrics or 'wipers' of Miller's loom. It was known at first as the crank loom to distinguish it from Miller's wiper loom, but now the crank is almost universally

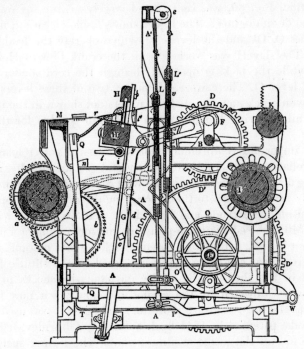

Figure 80   Sharp and Roberts' power loom, side elevation

used for this purpose. A perspective drawing of the loom, viewed from the front, is shown in Fig. 79. Eccentrics on the shaft D operated the levers F, F to raise and lower the heald shafts G, and the shuttle movements were obtained through the lever P, the cords Q, and the pickers R, the lever P being actuated from levers 2 (again raised and lowered by eccentrics on shaft D), rods 4, and connections 5 and 6. A. Buchanan, in Scotland, installed many of these looms in 1807 in his mill and worked them successfully, along with power-driven preparatory machines.[9]

In 1822, Richard Roberts, the inventor of the automatic mule, through his firm of Sharp and Roberts, in Manchester, constructed a loom[10] based on that of Horrocks, but embodying further improvements. Horrocks's loom was reputedly made mainly of metal, although the illustration does not support this view; possibly he began to use more metal later. Certainly Roberts's loom, judging by the illustration, Fig. 80, was constructed largely of iron, as was to be expected of an engineer. The figure shows a side elevation; note the eccentrics O, O[1] and the levers P[1] which operate the heald shafts L, L[1]. The slay H was worked from the crank F as in Horrocks's loom, while the picking operated through the cord shown on the vertical lever Q. There were, of course, two of these levers which were given quick movements from rollers not shown in the illustration, while a spring brought them back into position for the next pick.

Two important requirements for a successful power loom were (a) a reliable warp-protector motion and (b) an equally reliable stopping device on the failure of the weft supply. The early inventors certainly added devices to their looms for these purposes, but their mechanisms were crude and inefficient. Actually the principle on which Miller based his warp-protector motion was later improved upon, but in 1842 J. Bullough patented a 'loose reed motion', whereby the reed was caused to swing backwards if the shuttle became trapped in the shed.[11] The device obviated the shocks to which looms were subjected by the earlier motion (which now became known as the fast-reed warp protector) and when it was used with a loom brake patented in 1845 by J. Sellars,[12] of Burnley, it became possible to run the looms at almost double the former speed. The fast-reed motion is still used, however, in looms weaving heavy fabrics.

An automatic stop motion which operated on the failure of the weft was invented by J. Ramsbottom and R. Holt, both of Todmorden, Lancashire, in 1834.[13] It is mentioned as being the first example of the use of the 'weft fork' as a detecting device. It was later improved upon by W. Kenworthy and J. Bullough, of Blackburn, in 1841.[14] The weft fork was a small lever L on the loom frame which was formed with three prongs P. The prongs were normally prevented from passing through spaces in the reed R during the forward movement of the slay by the presence of the weft W (Fig. 81). If, however, the weft was missing, the lever was not tilted and the horizontal arm of the lever then impinged upon mechanism connected with the starting handle and stopped the loom. Simple though it appears, the reliability of the motion had an important influence on the development of the power loom. To quote one writer, 'Here at last, fifty-five years after the invention of the power

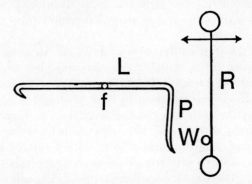

Figure 81   The weft fork motion

loom, was an improvement which had been the chief *desideratum* from Cartwright's days. Without it the power loom never could have entirely replaced the hand loom or have become the important machine it is to-day.'[4]

The 'drop box' was invented in 1760 by Robert Kay, a son of the inventor of the fly-shuttle attachment. It consisted of two or more shuttle boxes which could be moved vertically to bring different shuttles into use. Its principal use was that of introducing coloured weft-way stripes into the fabric, a process which hitherto could only be accomplished by the weaver stopping his loom and changing the shuttles by hand.

Cartwright applied a similar device to his power loom, but caused the boxes to move laterally. By using coloured striped warps these boxes could also, of course, be used to produce check designs. In 1834, L. Smith[15] invented a circular box motion, the different shuttles being brought into position by the rotation of the box.

Many other improvements were applied to power looms so that, whereas at first a weaver could tend only two looms, the greater efficiency of the looms rendered the work easier and weavers could tend four looms producing plain calicoes and similar cloths. For the same reasons weaving became mainly a woman's job, although men were retained for the weaving of heavier fabrics and on the more complicated looms such as jacquards.

There were many developments in loom construction and in weaving techniques for the production of special types of fabrics. The weaving of pile fabrics may be taken as an example, pile being the term applied to the tufts and loops which project from the surface of a fabric.

As early as the thirteenth century fabrics known as fustians were woven with such loops, which were sometimes left uncut and in other cases cut to present a brush-like surface. The loops, which were formed from the weft threads, were produced by so designing the fabric that the weft was 'floated' over several warp threads at intervals, and the cutting was done afterwards by laying the fabric on a table and cutting the rows of loops with a pointed knife.[16]

Much better-known pile fabrics are velvets or plushes, although it is not known where they were first produced. The pile was formed from the warp threads, the loops being produced by using wood rods or wires extending across the loom, and over which the threads were woven. As the rod or wire was withdrawn, so a row of loops remained, and if the loops required to be cut a knife attached to the end of the wire cut the loops as the wire was withdrawn. Of course, a ground weave with warp from another beam was needed to form a foundation for the fabric. In due course these velvets and plushes began to be woven on power looms and in 1849 a method of inserting and withdrawing the wires automatically was introduced.

Before this time, in 1838, a method of making cut pile fabrics by weaving two fabrics together was devised. The two fabrics were woven face to face, joined by the same set of warp threads passing across from one fabric to the other, and when the fabrics were severed, two pile fabrics resulted. It was only possible to use this method on hand looms until about 1857, when a power loom weaving face-to-face fabrics was invented by a Spaniard and later perfected in England. More information about this development is given in Chapter 25.

The Automatic Loom

For many years one important function of the weaving process continued to be performed by hand—this was the replenishing of the weft in the shuttle. During the nineteenth century over twenty attempts were made by inventors to mechanise this process, the action taking place either during a momentary stoppage of the loom or while the loom continued running. The inventions may be divided into two classes: (*a*) those in which the shuttle was removed and replaced by a recharged shuttle; and (*b*) those in which only the cop or pirn was changed. As long ago as 1840 a patent was taken out, in Britain, in which the shuttle-changing method was adopted, and in 1857 a cop-changing system was patented. But it was not until the 1890s that success was achieved, the inventor being James H. Northrop, a native of Keighley, Yorkshire, who had emigrated to the United States and whose name is perpetuated in the 'Northrop loom', a term now synonymous with 'automatic loom'.

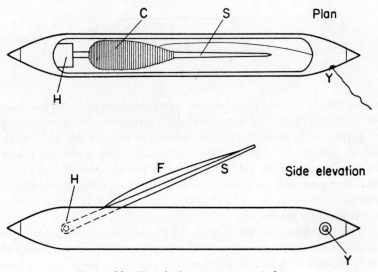

Figure 82   Shuttle for non-automatic loom

About 1891 he appears to have been undecided whether to work on the shuttle-changing or the cop-changing system—there were three patents taken out in that year, one of which was a shuttle changer and the other two cop or bobbin changers. In 1894, however, there was patented in Britain in the name of A. G. Brookes, as a communication from W. F. Draper, who was Northrop's employer, a cop- or bobbin-changing automatic loom which, in fact, became the Northrop loom.[17]

To bring about this action, Northrop made drastic changes in the orthodox shuttle. Instead of a hinged tongue S in the shuttle (Fig. 82) he fitted spring clips C inside (Fig. 83), and in place of the shuttle eye through which the weft had to be threaded by the weaver he formed a groove so shaped that the weft was drawn into it by the automatic mechanism. Cops were ready skewered on spindles, and the latter were fitted with rings. Where weft pirns were used,

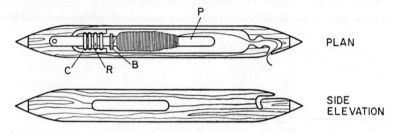

Figure 83   Shuttle for automatic loom

these, too, had metal rings at their base, as shown at R. To the loom, over one of the shuttle boxes, he added a magazine to store the cops or pirns, along with mechanism which, as soon as the weft on the cop or pirn in the shuttle was exhausted, pushed it out and pushed in a full cop or pirn, the rings R being forced between the clips C so that cop or pirns was firmly held. This action took place while the shuttle was in its box and without the need for stopping or even slowing down the loom.

There were other movements to mechanise, including the provision of a warp stop motion. Since the object of having an automatic weft-replenishing motion was that of enabling a weaver to tend more looms, he or she could not be expected to detect broken warp threads quickly and such a stopping device became a necessity. (It is interesting to note that although Cartwright and other early inventors of power looms patented warp-stop motions, subsequently, because a weaver only tended about four looms, and so was able to watch all the warps, they were in general not considered necessary.)

Many improvements were made on the Northrop loom, including one in which the change of cop or pirn took place, not through the

weft-fork motion but from a 'feeler' acting on the pirn, a feeler
which operated when the weft was almost, but not quite, exhausted.
By this means 'broken picks', i.e. gaps in the cloth where the weft
had ended, were obviated. Descriptions of this and other mechanisms
in detail will be found in the technical textbooks.

To summarise, an automatic loom is one which includes an automatic weft-replenishing mechanism; all power looms are automatic
in their other operations. Plate 30 gives a perspective view of a
Northrop loom; the circular magazine containing full pirns in position for transfer to the shuttle can be seen on the right, and below it
the receptacle for receiving the empty pirns ejected from the shuttle.

A number of other successful automatic looms have been invented
since the 1890s, some of them bobbin changers, others shuttle
changers, but to James H. Northrop belongs the credit of inventing
the first of these, a loom which is still used in large numbers
throughout the textile world.

CHAPTER TWENTY-FIVE

Titus Salt and Samuel C. Lister

In this chapter are described some of the achievements of two York-shiremen, born within a few years of each other in the early part of the nineteenth century and each having an important influence on the textile industry. There were other similarities: each per-severed in the face of many difficulties and discouragements, devised machinery and discovered a method of spinning a raw material hitherto looked upon as useless, and built up a large and important business. These concerns are still thriving and are known the world over. And as was to be expected from two such forceful and persever-ing men, they were also business rivals.

Titus Salt (1803–76) was born in Morley, near Bradford. It was during his boyhood and early manhood that the worsted industry was being diverted from Norwich to Bradford, and in 1824 he entered into partnership with his father in that trade. He soon showed an aptitude for business and, in particular, for experimenting with techniques for the production of yarns and fabrics made from raw materials previously considered unsuitable for textile processing. An early example of this activity was concerned with some kinds of Russian wool which were so harsh and tangled that worsted spinners declared them unspinnable. But young Salt experimented and perse-vered with the material, modifying and adapting existing machinery until he succeeded in producing marketable yarns. Increased trade for the firm followed, and by 1836 he had his own business with four mills in Bradford.[1] But a bigger success was to come, again as a result of experimental work. The material on this occasion was alpaca.

In 1807, some British troops returning from the fighting in Buenos Aires brought a few bags of alpaca, which is the fleece of the alpaca goat, a native of South America. The fibres were examined by experts, including spinners, and it was generally agreed that they could not be processed satisfactorily on existing machinery. For some

twenty years the matter was allowed to lapse.[2] Then more alpaca
reached the country and several manufacturers made attempts to
spin and weave it with varying degrees of success. Alpaca fibres are
very smooth and lustrous and it was essential that these characteristics should be retained in the fabrics produced so that they could be
seen as new effects. In general this result was not achieved.

In 1836 Titus Salt was informed of a consignment of 300 bales of
alpaca lying in Liverpool, with little chance of its being sold because
of the earlier failures to utilise it. Whether he had had some earlier
experience in processing the fibres or had only heard of the earlier
attempts is not clear; but he bought the entire consignment and
began experimenting.[3]

Dickens in *Household Words*, gives an account of the incident:

A huge pile of dirty looking sacks filled with some fibrous material
which had a strong resemblance to superannuated horsehair or
frowsy, elongated wool, was landed in Liverpool . . . The rats
appeared to be the only parties who approved at all of the importation. One day a plain, business-looking young man with an
intelligent face and quiet, reserved manner was walking alone
through these same warehouses. [When he saw the bales he took
a tuft of the material and] looked at it, rubbed it, pulled it about;
in fact, he did all but taste it, and he would have done that if it
had suited his purpose, for he was 'Yorkshire'.

The story continues with the statement that the young man
offered eightpence a pound for the stuff, an offer which was at once
accepted and which so staggered the principals that after the buyer
had departed they gave the staff a holiday!

In his experiments the principal machine modifications the 'young
man' made were on his wool-combing machines and on his gill boxes,
adapting them for the smoother, straighter, and more lustrous fibres.
He eventually succeeded and it is probable that some of the reward
for this success was due to the introduction about that time of cotton
warps in the worsted industry. He used these warps with alpaca weft
yarns and so established another important branch to his business.
For some time he was the only spinner of alpaca in Bradford. As a
result of this and other developments he built a large new factory in
1851–53 outside Bradford, near the River Aire. He also built houses

there for the operatives and the new town was named Saltaire. The factory was built to the highest standards of the times, with maximum provisions for natural light, warmth, and ventilation. One novel feature was the placing of the driving shafting and pulleys under the floor instead of overhead. The arrangement gave uninterrupted light for the workers from the roof lights and probably reduced the risk of accidents. But maintenance would be more difficult and the idea does not seem to have been applied by many other manufacturers. By 1871 a church, hospital, baths, and schools had been established in the town.[4]

Throughout his life Titus Salt demonstrated by this kind of development his interest in and care for his workpeople. He was created a baronet in 1869.

Samuel C. Lister

Samuel Cunliffe Lister (1815–1906) was born at Calverly Hall, near Bradford. As a young man he made frequent visits to North America while in the employment of a Liverpool merchanting firm, and these experiences probably developed his business acumen to a considerable degree. The family was wealthy and the father financed the building of a worsted mill for him and his brother at Manningham, near Bradford, a partnership which lasted until 1845. For a few subsequent years he was in partnership with others, but from 1864 he carried on his business without partners. In 1889, Manningham Mills became a limited company, of which he remained the principal stockholder and chairman.

He was a hard bargainer in business, but he was also that rather unusual combination of businessman and inventor, taking out more than a hundred and fifty patents during his lifetime. His name is associated with several branches of the textile industry; one of these being that of wool combing (see Chapter 23). Another branch was that of silk combing or dressing, and it is of interest to note his reactions when he first examined some waste silk.

He recalls being handed some of this material which 'looked like oakum' in 1857. It was a sample imported from India and was probably of a much lower quality, from a spinner's point of view, than the usual qualities being spun at the time. The following account of Lister's experience seems to have been inspired by Dickens's description of Titus Salt's first purchase of alpaca:

One day, while strolling round a warehouse in London, he came upon a heap of rubbishy-looking stuff not unlike the sweepings of a warehouse floor. It was an odd collection consisting of bits of stick, dead leaves, ends of twine, dirty flocks, crushed worms and silk fibre, all stuck together by gummy matter . . . (he) enquired what use was made of it, 'Oh, we sell it as rubbish', was the reply . . . The vendor was glad to part with it at a halfpenny a pound.[5]

Methods of softening and removing the gummy matter and of cleaning the waste were already known, and Lister decided that what was required was an effective combing machine which would not only further clean and straighten the fibres but would also remove the shorter ones. No doubt his earlier experiences in the invention of wool-combing machines influenced him in this decision. Along with J. Warburton he constructed a silk-combing machine in 1859, but the inventors found it to be *too* effective. The yarns produced from the combed silk were of exceptionally high quality, but the amount of waste rejected by the combing machine was so great that economically the results were a failure.

Lister now turned his attention to another form of combing silk, the dressing process described in Chapter 17. His efforts were successful and he soon built up a very profitable business in silk spinning and weaving.

During the 1860s he became interested in reports from his Manningham Mills manager regarding a loom which the latter had seen working in Spain. Lister had been engaged on weaving velvets and plushes for many years, as indicated by the publication of patents in his name during the previous decade, but these were concerned with the use of pile rods or wires and not with the weaving of 'face-to-face' fabrics (see Chapter 24), in which he now became interested. The loom was invented by Barrau y Cortes[6] and the British patent was taken out in 1858 as a communication by G. Davies.[7] Jose Reixach, who owned a weaving mill in Spain, tried to develop the loom, but got into financial difficulties, and it was at this point that Lister bought the patent rights and brought Reixach to Bradford to continue his efforts along with those of himself and his staff. One of the problems was that of cutting the fabric so as to produce a level pile, and Lister is said to have got inspiration from watching a scissors grinder in the street.[8] He had previously been using stones to sharpen the cutters, and he now replaced these with small emery wheels, which gave much better results.

But the developments in general proved to be difficult, extending over eleven years and costing Lister some £29,000. He took out a number of patents on the loom in his own name in 1868 and 1869,[9] while in 1871 he took one out jointly with José Reixach y Gispert.[10] Once success was achieved, however, the sums he had expended were more than recouped each year for many years from the sale of the products of the looms,[11] and the name Lister became famous through the world in its association with reasonably priced high-quality velvets and plushes.

In 1891 he became the first Baron Masham.

CHAPTER TWENTY-SIX

The Present and the Future

In the main the present-day practice in the processing of textile productions has been reached by normal evolutionary changes; but the indications now are that future methods will be largely of a revolutionary nature.

At present opening and cleaning of the natural fibres have followed the lines of the early methods—for example, beating over gridded surfaces and the use of air currents in the case of cotton. Similarly, cotton continues to be carded on revolving flat carding machines, wool and other fibres on roller and clearer machines. Wool is still mainly combed on the Noble comb, invented in 1853, and subsequent worsted processes include gill boxes and the cap spinning frame, invented in 1828, or the mule. Wool is carded on the condenser system, and spun on the mule or a modified ring frame. Cotton is prepared for spinning on flyframes and spun on ring frames or mules, the latter now mainly used only for the finest counts of yarn. Flax until recently was being spun on flyer spinning frames, but various modifications have now made it possible to spin these yarns on ring frames. Similar conditions apply to the other sections of the industry, e.g. nett silk, spun silk, and the processes used in twisting man-made fibres.

The preparation of yarns for weaving and knitting is also carried out in principle as in earlier days, with winding and, where required, warping, beaming, and sizing, or dressing machines. But there have been remarkable changes from the simple machines used until the early decades of the present century, especially in the winding processes. They are now often almost completely automatic in action; yarn packages are supplied to the machines, completed packages are removed from the machines, and replaced by empty package centres, all automatically. Similarly, broken threads are re-tied mechanically and, in some cases, weft is wound on to pirns in the actual loom, to be inserted in the shuttle at the required time.

The great majority of woven fabrics are produced on looms, either non-automatic or automatic, in which conventional shuttles and shuttle-projecting mechanisms are used.

Knitting is still carried out on straight machines, on machines producing fully-fashioned fabrics, on warp-knitting machines, and on circular machines. The needles are either of the bearded type, devised by William Lee in 1589, or of the latch type invented in 1856. A tubular needle patented some thirty years ago, although introducing a new method of closing the hook, still retained the bearded construction.

About a hundred and fifty years ago the inventors were skilled craftsmen—reed-makers, frameworkers, clockmakers, weavers, carpenters, and mechanics (with the suprising exception of at least two divines and a barber!). Later, skilled mechanics in the employ of machine-makers and, more recently, highly trained mechanical engineers were in the main the inventors who improved the early machines or devised new ones. But the future inventor is more likely to be an authority on physics, hydraulics, aerodynamics, electronics, and other branches of science.

It is possible, perhaps probable, that many of the mechanical means now used in the production of textile goods will have disappeared from the mills in the not-far-distant future. Researches and experiments are taking place in various parts of the world in efforts to simplify these processes and, more important, to introduce new techniques.

In spinning, methods of producing yarns on entirely different principles are being tried. Amongst these are the use of air currents and the breaking off of the sliver so that only tufts of fibres are fed forward. Twisting methods described earlier involved either rotating the delivery package or the feed package. By the break system twist can be inserted by rotating the yarn at the break point—a considerable simplification of this important process.

In weaving, attempts have been made for many years to dispense with the shuttle. The propulsion of the shuttle normally requires mechanism which is intermittent and jerky in action, resulting in excessive wear and limiting the loom speed. A small proportion of the world's looms are now working in which the shuttle has been dispensed with. The weft is supplied from large packages on one or both sides of the loom and is conveyed across the loom in some cases by levers, in others by the use of small carriers which are shot at high speeds across the loom by pneumatic or other forces. The future, however, holds possibilities for inserting the weft without any carrier. Amongst the methods which have been patented are air streams and jets of water; the direct projection of the weft from rotating discs and cones is also being tried.

In the knitting section attempts are being made to produce fabrics without the use of the orthodox hooked needle, whether bearded or latched. It is again a movement away from the orthodox, but whether the method will be an improvement on present methods cannot yet be foreseen.

In the field of synthetic fibres and filaments there is little doubt that more of these will be produced involving different chemical formulae from such established products as nylon and Terylene, and having different characteristics.

To summarise, the future of the textile industry appears as a vision of more new raw materials, of spinning without spindles, weaving without shuttles and (though this is much more problematical) knitting without needles. Such changes surely merit the description 'revolutionary'.

Source References

CHAPTER ONE

1 John Dyer, *The Fleece*, 1757.
2 J. Horner, *The Linen Trade of Europe during the Spinning Wheel Period*, 1920.
3 C. Gill, *The Rise of the Irish Linen Industry*, 1925.
4 J. James, 'The Reminiscences of an Octogenarian' in *The History of the Worsted Manufacture*, 1857.

CHAPTER TWO

1 C. Deering, *A History of Nottingham*, 1751.
2 J. Blackner, *History of Nottingham*, 1816.
3 G. Henson, *A History of Framework Knitting and Lace Trades*, 1831.
4 W. Felkin, *A History of Machine Wrought Hosiery and Lace Manufactures*, 1867.

CHAPTER THREE

1 V. Zonca, *Novo Teatro di Machine*, 1607, 1621, and 1656.
2 S. N. Clark, *Science and Social Welfare in the Age of Newton*, 1937.
3 *B.P. 422, A.D. 1718.*
4 A description of the deeds is to be seen in the Archives Department of the Central Library, Leeds.
5 P. Mantoux, *The Industrial Revolution in the Eighteenth Century*, 1961.
6 W. Hutton, *The History of Derby*, 1791.
7 D. P. Davies, *View of Derbyshire*, 1811.
8 G. B. Hill, Ed., *Boswell's Life of Johnson*, vol. III, 1887.

CHAPTER FOUR

1 Wadsworth and Mann, *The Cotton Trade and Industrial Lancashire*, 1600–1780.
2 *B.P. 542, A.D. 1733.*
3 F. Espinasse, *Lancashire Worthies*, 1874.
4 J. Lord, *Memoir of John Kay*, 1903.
5 B. Woodcroft, *Brief Biographies of Inventors of Machines for the Manufacture of Textile Fabrics*, 1863.

CHAPTER FIVE

1 Robert Cole, *Some Account of Lewis Paul*, read at a meeting of the British Association for the Advancement of Science, at Leeds, September 1858.
   Also as an Appendix to G. J. French, *The Life and Times of Samuel Crompton*, 1859.
2 *B.P. 562, A.D. 1738.*
3 *B.P. 724, A.D. 1758.*
4 J. James, *History of the Worsted Manufacture*, 1857.
5 H. Heaton, *The Yorkshire Woollen and Worsted Industries*, 1965.

CHAPTER SIX

1 W. Felkin, *A History of Machine Wrought Hosiery and Lace Manufactures*, 1867.
2 *B.P. 722, A.D. 1758.*
3 *B.P. 734, A.D. 1759.*
4 *B.P. 1161, A.D. 1777.*

CHAPTER SEVEN

1 F. Espinasse, *Lancashire Worthies*, 1874.
2 A. Ure, *The Cotton Manufacture of Great Britain*, 1836.
3 W. B. Crump, Ed., *The Leeds Woollen Industry*, 1931.
4 C. Aspin and S. D. Chapman, *James Hargreaves and the Spinning Jenny*, 1964.
5 R. Guest, *A Compendious History of the Cotton Manufacture*, 1823.

6 From a statement written by Mary Burgess, Hargreaves's daughter, in 1822, and found at the Peel Park Library, Salford, stuck in the back of a book which once belonged to Joseph Brotherton, M.P. for the city. See *The Guardian*, 16 June 1967.
7 W. A. Hunter, 'James Hargreaves and the Invention of the Spinning Jenny', *Transactions of the Newcomen Society*, vol. XXVIII, 1951–3.
8 G. Henson, *History of the Framework Knitters*, 1831.
9 *B.P. 1018, A.D. 1772.*

CHAPTER EIGHT

1 P. Whittle, *The History of the Borough of Preston*, 1837.
2 *B.P. 931, A.D. 1769.*
3 R. S. Fitton and A. P. Wadsworth, *The Strutts and the Arkwrights, 1758–1830*, 1958.
4 *Rees' Cyclopaedia*, 1819.
5 *B.P. 1111, A.D. 1775.*
6 *B.P. 1212, A.D. 1779.*
7 E. Baines, *History of Cotton Manufacture in Great Britain*, 1835.
8 *The Trial of a Cause*, 1785.
9 P. Mantoux, *The Industrial Revolution in the Eighteenth Century*, 1961.

CHAPTER NINE

1 John Kennedy, 'A Brief Memoir of Samuel Crompton', *Memoirs of the Literary and Philosophical Society of Manchester*, second series, vol. V, 1831.
2 G. J. French, *The Life and Times of Samuel Crompton*, 1859.
3 B. P. Dobson, *The Story of the Evolution of the Spinning Machine*, 1910.
4 *B.P. 1879, A.D. 1792.*
5 E. Baines, *History of the Cotton Manufacture of Great Britain*, 1855.

CHAPTER TEN

1 B. P. Dobson, *The Story of the Evolution of the Spinning Machine*, 1910.

2 C. Aspin and S. D. Chapman, *James Hargreaves and the Spinning Jenny*, 1964.
3 *B.P. 628, A.D. 1748.*
4 *B.P. 636, A.D. 1748.*
5 *Rees' Cyclopaedia*, 1819.
6 *B.P. 1212, A.D. 1779.*
7 G. J. French, *The Life and Times of Samuel Crompton*, 1859.
8 *The Trial of a Cause*, Court of King's Bench, 25 June 1785.
9 W. B. Crump, Ed., *The Leeds Woollen Industry*, 1931.
10 *B.P. 4875, A.D. 1823.*
11 *B.P. 13027, A.D. 1850.*

CHAPTER ELEVEN

1 J. Beckmann, *History of Inventions, Discoveries and Origins*, 1846.
2 A. Barlow, *The History of Principles of Weaving*, 1879, 1884.
3 *B.P. 1083, A.D. 1774.*
4 'Cotton Manufacture', *Encyclopaedia Britannica*, Seventh Edition.
5 *B.P. 1470, A.D. 1785.*
6 *B.P. 1565, A.D. 1786.*
7 *B.P. 1616, A.D. 1787.*
8 *B.P. 1676, A.D. 1788.*
9 R. Guest, *A Compendious History of the Cotton Manufacture*, 1823.
10 A. P. Usher, *A History of Mechanical Inventions*, 1958.
11 P. Mantoux, *The Industrial Revolution in the Eighteenth Century*, 1961.
12 M. Strickland, *A Memoir of Edmund Cartwright, D.D.*, 1843.

CHAPTER TWELVE

1 John Dyer, *The Fleece*, 1757.
2 W. B. Crump, Ed., *The Leeds Woollen History 1780–1820*, 1931.
3 A. Barlow, *The History and Principles of Weaving*, 1879, 1884.
4 *B.P. 2084, A.D. 1803.*
5 *B.P. 2771, A.D. 1804.*
6 W. Radcliffe, *Origin of the New System of Manufacture*, 1828.

7 P. Gaskell, *Artisans and Machinery*, 1836.
8 G. Unwin, *Samuel Oldknow and the Arkwrights*, 1924.

CHAPTER THIRTEEN

1 J. James, *History of the Worsted Manufacture*, 1857.
2 B.P. 7529, A.D. 1838.
3 T. W. Fox, *The Mechanism of Weaving*, 1922.
4 A. Barlow, *The History and Principles of Weaving*, 1879, 1884.
5 B.P. 1946, A.D. 1858.
6 B.P. 4951, A.D. 1824.
7 B.P. 257, A.D. 1687.
8 B.P. 4162, A.D. 1817.

CHAPTER FOURTEEN

1 Thomas Deloney, *The Pleasant History of Jack o' Newbury*.
2 W. Felkin, *A History of Machine Wrought Hosiery and Lace Manufacture*, 1867.
3 R. S. Fitton and A. P. Wadsworth, *The Strutts and the Arkwrights*, 1958.
4 P. Mantoux, *The Industrial Revolution in the Eighteenth Century*, 1961.
5 Report of the 1816 Committee.
6 C. Aspen and S. D. Chapman, *James Hargreaves and the Spinning Jenny*, 1964.
7 Robert Owen, *The Life of Robert Owen*, 1857.
8 G. Unwin, *Samuel Oldknow and the Arkwrights*, 1924.
9 C. Gill, *The Rise of the Irish Linen Industry*, 1925.
10 J. James, *History of the Worsted Manufacture*, 1857.
11 B. P. Dobson, *The Story of the Evolution of the Spinning Machine*, 1911.

CHAPTER FIFTEEN

1 H. Heaton, *The Yorkshire Woollen and Worsted Industry*, 1965.
2 H. Hamilton, *The Industrial Revolution in Scotland*, 1966.
3 G. Unwin, *Samuel Oldknow and the Arkwrights*, 1924.
4 C. Gill, *The Rise of the Irish Linen Industry*, 1925.
5 P. Gaskell, *Artisans and Machinery*. 1836.

6 P. Mantoux, *The Industrial Revolution in the Eighteenth Century*, 1961.
7 R. W. Cooke Taylor, *The Modern Factory System*, 1891.
8 J. James, *History of the Worsted Manufacture*, 1857.
9 B. P. Dobson, *The Story of the Evolution of the Spinning Machine*, 1911.
10 S. D. Chapman, *Journal of Industrial Archaeology*, vol. 2, No. 3, Sutton Old Mill.
11 R. A. Arnold, *History of the Cotton Famine*, 1864.

CHAPTER SIXTEEN

1 A. Ure, *The Cotton Manufacture of Great Britain*, vol. II, 1861.
2 *B.P. 2571, A.D. 1803.*
3 W. Felkin, *A History of Machine Wrought Hosiery and Lace Manufacture*, 1867.
4 *Introduction to Abridgements to Patent Specifications Relating to Lace Making, Knitting, etc., 1675–1866*, 2nd edition, 1879.
5 *B.P. 3151, A.D. 1808.*
6 *B.P. 3216, A.D. 1809.*
7 Z. Halls, *Machine Made Lace in Nottingham*, 1964.
8 *B.P. 5103 and 5144, A.D. 1825.*
9 W. G. Allen, *John Heathcoat and his Heritage*, 1958.

CHAPTER SEVENTEEN

1 F. Warner, *The Silk Industry*, 1921.
2 *B.P. 165, A.D. 1671.*
3 *B.P. 7228, A.D. 1836.*
4 H. Raynor, *Silk Throwing and Waste Silk Spinning*, 1903.
5 W. English, 'The Silk Industry', *History of Technology*, vol. IV, Ed. C. J. Singer, 1958.
6 *B.P. 3600, A.D. 1877.*
7 *B.P. 141 and 2194, A.D. 1868.*
8 R. Badnall, *A View of the Silk Trade*, 1828.

CHAPTER EIGHTEEN

1 J. James, *History of the Worsted Manufacture*, 1857.

2 W. B. Crump, Ed., *The Leeds Woollen Industry, 1780–1920,* 1931.

3 *Rees' Cyclopaedia,* 1819.

4 G. Unwin, *Samuel Oldknow and the Arkwrights,* 1924.

5 *B.P. 1130, A.D. 1776.*

6 *B.P. 5486, A.D. 1827.*

7 *B.P. 1761, A.D. 1836.*

8 *B.P. 7318, A.D. 1837.*

9 *B.P. 7374, A.D. 1837.*

10 J. A. Iredale, 'The Last Two Piecing Machines', *Industrial Archaeology,* 1967 Ed. K. Hudson.

11 *B.P. 5819, A.D. 1840.*

12 W. P. Crankshaw, *Report on a Survey of the Welsh Textile Industry,* 1927.

13 E. Law, *The Textile Manufacturer,* vol. 7, p. 248, 1881.

14 *B.P. 673, A.D. 1859.*

15 R. S. Fitton and A. P. Wadsworth, *The Strutts and the Arkwrights, 1758–1830,* 1958.

16 *B.P. 6741, A.D. 1834.*

17 *B.P. 6464, A.D. 1833.*

18 *B.P. 13794, A.D. 1851.*

19 W. Felkin, *A History of Machine Wrought Hosiery and Lace Manufacture,* 1867.

CHAPTER NINETEEN

1 C. Gill, *The Rise of the Irish Linen Industry,* 1925.

2 *B.P. 2034, A.D. 1795.*

3 *B.P. 2533, A.D. 1801.*

4 *B.P. 1613, A.D. 1787.*

5 J. Horner, *The Linen Trade of Europe During the Spinning Wheel Period,* 1920.

6 *B.P. 1752, A.D. 1790.*

7 *B.P. 3855, A.D. 1814.*

8 *B.P. 5226, A.D. 1825.*

9 T. Mackay, Ed., *The Autobiography of Samuel Smiles,* 1905.

10 W. Charley, *Flax and Its Products in Ireland,* 1862.

11 *B.P. 1898, A.D. 1839.*

12 *B.P. 2190, A.D. 1854.*

13 T. Woodhouse and A. Briand, *A Century of Progress in Jute Manufacture*, 1934.

CHAPTER TWENTY

1 *B.P. 5787, A.D. 1829.*
2 Evan Leigh, *The Science of Cotton Spinning*, 1873.
3 R. Marsden, *Cotton Spinning*, 1909.
4 *B.P. 5822, A.D. 1829.*
5 J. James, *History of the Worsted Manufacture*, 1857.
6 T. Baines, *Yorkshire Past and Present*, vol. II, 1877.
7 *B.P. 5316, A.D. 1826.*
8 *B.P. 4807, A.D. 1823.*
9 *B.P. 5217, A.D. 1825.*
10 *B.P. 6497, A.D. 1892.*
11 *B.P. 122, A.D. 1858.*
12 W. English, 'History of Winding', *Journal of the Textile Institute*, vol. 49, no. 5.

CHAPTER TWENTY-ONE

1 *Proceedings of the Manchester Literary and Philosophical Society*, 1864.
2 *Transactions*, Society of Engineers, Manchester, January 1887.
3 S. Smiles, *Lives of the Engineers*, 1861.
4 *B.P. 4726, A.D. 1822.*
5 *B.P. 5138, A.D. 1825.*
6 *B.P. 5949, A.D. 1830.*
7 *Transactions of the Newcomen Society*, vol. XXX, 1945–46.

CHAPTER TWENTY-TWO

1 *Introduction to Abridgements of Patent Specifications relating to Lace Making, Knitting, etc., 1675–1866*, 2nd edition, 1879.
2 *B.P. 1820, A.D. 1791.*
3 W. Felkin, *A History of Machine Wrought Hosiery and Lace Manufacture*, 1867.
4 *B.P. 3993, A.D. 1816.*
5 *B.P. 11899, A.D. 1847.*
6 *B.P. 2745, A.D. 1855.*

7 *B.P. 1858, A.D. 1856.*
8 *B.P. 1660, A.D. 1851; B.P. 70, A.D. 1860; B.P. 1901, A.D. 1863.*
9 *B.P. 4037, A.D. 1816.*

CHAPTER TWENTY-THREE

1 *B.P. 1747 and 1787, A.D. 1790; B.P. 1876, A.D. 1792.*
2 J. James, *History of the Worsted Manufacture*, 1857.
3 *B.P. 5560, A.D. 1827.*
4 A. Ure, *The Philosophy of Manufactures*, 1835.
5 *B.P. 9404, A.D. 1842; B.P. 9996, B.P. 9780, A.D. 1843.*
6 *B.P. 12712, A.D. 1849; B.P. 13009, A.D. 1850; B.P. 13532, A.D. 1851; B.P. 14135, A.D. 1852.*
7 *B.P. 11103, A.D. 1846.*
8 J. R. Hunt, *Worsted Combing and Carding*, 1932.
9 *B.P. 890, B.P. 894, A.D. 1853.*
10 *B.P. 1058, A.D. 1856.*
11 James Burnley, *The History of Wool and Wool Combing*, 1889.

CHAPTER TWENTY-FOUR

1 *B.P. 12997, A.D. 1850.*
2 *B.P. 5059, A.D. 1883.*
3 *B.P. 8226, A.D. 1839.*
4 R. Marsden, *Cotton Weaving*, 1895.
5 *B.P. 2293, A.D. 1852.*
6 H. Nisbet, *Preliminary Operations of Weaving*, vol. I, 1914.
7 *B.P. 1517, A.D. 1857.*
8 *B.P. 2699, A.D. 1803.*
9 H. Hamilton, *The Industrial Revolution in Scotland*, 1966.
10 *B.P. 4726, A.D. 1822.*
11 *B.P. 9507, A.D. 1842.*
12 *B.P. 10563, A.D. 1845.*
13 *B.P. 6644, A.D. 1834.*
14 *B.P. 18790, A.D. 1841.*
15 *B.P. 9940, A.D. 1843.*
16 A. Barlow, *The History and Principles of Weaving*, 1884.
17 *B.P. 22939, A.D. 1894.*

CHAPTER TWENTY-FIVE

1 R. Balgarnie, *Sir Titus Salt, His Life and its Lessons*, 1877.
2 J. James, *History of the Worsted Manufacture*, 1857.
3 F. Warner, *The Silk Industry*, 1921.
4 A. Holroyd, *Saltaire and its Founder*, 1871.
5 W. Cudworth, *Worstedopolis*, 1888.
6 A. Latore, *C.I.B.A. Review*, no. 96, February 1953, 'Velvet'.
7 *B.P. 2429, A.D. 1858.*
8 *Lister Magazine*, no. 144, December 1967.
9 *B.P. 470, 2386, 2429, 3669, A.D. 1868; B.P. 1549, A.D. 1869.*
10 *B.P. 1117, A.D. 1871.*
11 Lord Masham, *Lord Masham's Inventions*, 1905.

Glossary of Technical Terms

In general, technical terms have been explained in the text as they occurred. The following are defined for quick reference.

BATTEN. n. See SLAY.

BEAM. n. A roller on which a series of yarns are wound side by side. A weaver's beam carries the warp (q.v.) yarns and is mounted at the supply side of the loom.

BEARDED NEEDLE. n. A needle used in machine knitting, in which the hook can be closed by pressure, but is sufficiently elastic to open when the pressure is removed. See PRESSER and LATCH NEEDLE.

CARRIAGE (MULE). n. That part of the mule which carries the spindles and moves away from and towards the drawing rollers.

COP. n. A cylindrical package of yarn, with conical ends, as formed by winding on the spindle in mule spinning.

CREEL. n. A frame for holding supply bobbins and other yarn packages as these unwind to deliver yarns to the processing machine.

DENIER. n. A term denoting the fineness of silk and man-made filament yarns. Thus the weight in grammes of 9,000 metres of yarn is the 'denier' of that yarn, e.g. '150 denier'.

DEVIL. n. A term at one time applied to opening and cleaning machines in the cotton, wool, and corresponding waste industries.

DRAWBAR. n. The bar carrying the clasp on the jenny. It is drawn away from the spindles during the twisting operation and pushed towards them during the winding.

DRESSING. n. 1. The application of an adhesive paste to yarns to facilitate the weaving process.

2. The arranging and winding on a beam (q.v.) of a number of yarns from ball or chain warps (q.v.) in preparation for weaving.

225

3. A combing process applied to waste silks on a dressing machine.

FALLERS. n. 1. Gills (q.v.) which on reaching the end of their combing movement descend (hence the name) to return to the beginning of the movement.

2. Levers which carry wires extending along the mule adjacent to the spindles. Winding faller wires guide the yarn on to the cop (q.v.); counter faller wires control yarn tensions—both actions taking place during the winding operation.

FLYER. n. A device resembling an inverted U which fits on to a spindle. It assists in the twisting and winding of slubbings (q.v.), rovings (q.v.), and yarns.

FRAMEWORKER. n. One who operates a stocking frame.

GILLS. n. Metal bars fitted with rows of pins. They travel between drawing rollers in order to comb and control the fibres. See FALLERS.

GIN. n. A machine which detaches cotton fibres from their seeds.

HEALD. n. A cord formed with an eyelet through which a warp (q.v.) yarn is passed. In the loom these healds are raised and lowered to allow the passage of the shuttle between the warp yarns.

HEDDLE. n. See HEALD.

LATCH NEEDLE. n. A needle used in machine knitting in which the hook is opened and closed by the movement of a pivoted lever (the 'latch'). See BEARDED NEEDLE.

LEASE. n. The separation of warp (q.v.) yarns, or of groups of yarns by cords or rods. Thus a yarn or group of yarns may be passed over the cord or rod and the adjacent yarn or group passed under the rod. By this means an orderly arrangement of the warp yarns is maintained and the work of the operative facilitated.

NETT SILK. n. Silk yarns produced by twisting together the filaments unwound from the cocoons of silkworms. See THROWING.

NOILS. n. Short wool or silk fibres removed by the combing or dressing machine. See TOPS.

ORGANZINE. n. Nett silk yarns intended for use as warp (q.v.).

PICK. v. To pass a yarn across a loom between the warp (q.v.) yarns. See HEALD.

PICK. n. A length of weft (q.v.) in a woven fabric.

PICKER. n. An attachment in direct contact with the shuttle as it is sent across the loom.

PICKING PEG. n. Part of John Kay's invention of the fly shuttle. It is a stick which the weaver used to throw the shuttle from side to side, being connected by cords to the pickers (q.v.). When looms became power driven it became known as a picking stick.

PIECE. n. A specific length of fabric.

PIRN. n. A bobbin of relatively small diameter on which weft (q.v.) is wound. Its size and shape are devised for use in a shuttle.

PRESSER. n. A device on a knitting machine which closes the hook on a bearded needle (q.v.).

REED. n. Originally a frame fitted with split reeds, now wires, set close together and carried on the slay (q.v.) of a loom. Its main functions are to keep the warp (q.v.) yarns passing between the wires separate and to push the weft (q.v.) into place in the fabric.

ROVING. n. A fibrous, soft-twisted strand, so prepared for the spinning process. See SLUBBING.

SCUTCHER. n. A machine the essential feature of which was a rotating beater which struck fibrous material in order to loosen it and release impurities. Used especially in the flax and cotton industries.

SINKERS. n. Devices in knitting machines which deflect the yarn to be knitted from a straight line to form kinks preparatory to the interlooping action of knitting.

SLAY. n. A loom part, between the healds (q.v.) and the woven fabric, which oscillates backwards and forwards. It carries the reed (q.v.) and normally supports the shuttle.

SLEY. n. See SLAY.

SLIVER. n. A loose, untwisted strand of fibres, formed in preparation for drawing out into slubbing (q.v.) and roving (q.v.).

SLUBBING. n. A fibrous, soft-twisted strand, usually prepared for drawing out into roving (q.v.).

TAPPETS. n. Cams in a loom which through levers give the up-and-down movements to the healds (q.v.).

THROSTLE. n. The name given to the water frame (q.v.) after it had been converted to steam driving.

THROWING. n. The process of twisting nett silk (q.v.) and other man-made filaments to produce yarns.

TOPS. n. Slivers (q.v.) of wool which have been combed. See NOILS.

TRAM. n. Nett silk yarns (q.v.) used as weft (q.v.).

WARP. n. 1. Yarns prepared to be used as the lengthways threads in weaving and in warp knitting.

2. The lengthways yarns in a woven fabric.

WATER FRAME. n. The name by which Arkwright's spinning machine become known when it was turned by water power.

WEFT. n. 1. Yarns intended to be used as the transverse threads in weaving.

2. The transverse yarns in a woven fabric.

WILLOW. n. A name formerly applied to machines used in the opening and cleaning of cotton.

WILLY. n. A machine for opening out and loosening wool.

WIPER. n. A cam (obsolete).

Gazetteer

A List of Museums

with Textile Exhibits

Bath. The American Museum in Britain, Claverton Manor. A large number of textile materials of American origin, mostly early nineteenth century.

The Museum of Costume, Assembly Rooms.

Bedford. Bedford Museum, The Embankment. Pillows, patterns, bobbins and a bobbin-turning machine, relating to the pillow-lace industry.

Belfast. Ulster Museum, Stranmillis, 9. The Horner collection of spinning wheels from various countries. Early spinning, winding, and warping machines; hand and power looms. All connected with the flax industry. Damasks, lace, quilts, embroidery, and costumes from various countries.

Birmingham. Avery Historical Museum, Soho Foundry, 40. Early wool scales and weights. Docketed information on John Wyatt, associated with Lewis Paul in the invention of the first roller spinning machine.

City Museum and Art Gallery, 3. A skein of yarn spun by John Wyatt on the Paul and Wyatt roller spinning machine.

Blackburn. Lewis Textile Museum, Exchange Street. Working reconstructions and originals of early cotton spinning and weaving machines. Reconstructed interior of weaver's cottage before the Industrial Revolution.

Bolton. Hall-i'-th'-Wood Museum, Crompton By-Pass. Home of Samuel Crompton at the time of his invention of the mule. Now a folk museum representing the furniture and equipment (including a spinning wheel) used during the time of Crompton and earlier.

Textile Machinery Museum, Library Annex, Tong Moor Road. Jersey and Saxony spinning wheels, jenny, water frame, carding

229

engines from Belper and Cromford mills. Crompton's mule, lantern frame, and other early textile machines. (Note: New premises are being sought for these exhibits, and may be established at an early date. Inquiries should be addressed to the Curator, Museum and Art Gallery, Civic Centre, Bolton.)

Bradford. City Art Gallery and Museum. (A suitable building is being sought for use as an Industrial Museum. Exhibits of textile interest are at present stored away, but will be available for display when a building is found. A few of these are listed below.) Hand combs, flyer spinning and twisting frames, semi-automatic spinning mule, hand looms with jacquards.

Colne, Lancashire. The Colne Museum, Albert Road. A rope-making machine.

Coventry. Herbert Art Gallery and Museum, Jordan Well. Hand ribbon loom, jacquard ribbon looms, winding machines. Silk ribbons and pattern books.

Derby. County Borough of Derby Museum and Art Gallery, Strand. Early sewing machines, winding machines, cord-twisting machine.

Dumfries. Dumfries Burgh Museum, The Observatory. Spinning wheels, wool cards, heckling combs, linen-weaver's brush. Dresses and linen napkins.

Edinburgh. The Royal Scottish Museum, Department of Technology, Chamber Street, 1. Carding machines, wool combs, spinning wheels, hand looms, knitting machines.

Godalming. Godalming Museum, Bridge Street. Hand knitting frame, two needle moulds.

Halifax. Bankfield Museum. Textile implements from primitive societies throughout the world. Nineteenth- and twentieth-century textile machinery, including spinning wheels, jennies, mules, carding and combing implements, piecing machines, hand looms, flying shuttle looms, power-driven looms, warping mills, cropping and finishing machines. Over 5,000 fabric and costume samples.

Hawkshead, Westmorland. The Courthouse. Spinning materials and equipment, including two Saxony wheels from 'The Spinnery', Bowness (in use there until the end of the nineteenth century).

Helmshore, Lancashire. T.M.M. (Research) Museum, Holcombe Road. Spinning wheels, reconstructed Hargreaves jenny, early Arkwright carding, lapping, drawing and spinning machines from Cromford Mill.

Higher Mill. Built in 1789 as a fulling mill, now housing textile machines and expected later to become the first completemuse um of early textile history.

Hereford. Hereford City Library, Museum, Art Gallery and Old House, Broad Street. Spinning wheels, cottage weaver's loom from Brecon.

Huddersfield. The Tolson Memorial Museum, Ravensknowle. Spinning wheel, spinning jenny, hank winding or reeling machine, bobbin-winding frame, warping frame, jacquard loom.

Keighley. Art Gallery and Museum, Cliffe Castle. Hand wool comber's equipment, spinning wheels, jenny, winding machine, spindles and flyers, hand loom, shuttles, including a wheel shuttle, braiding machine.

Kendal. Abbott Hall Museum. A hand loom. Nineteenth-century textile materials, including linen and fine silks.

Leamington Spa. Public Library, Art Gallery and Museum, Avenue Road. Winding wheel, lace-making cushions and bobbins. Early costume.

Leeds. City Museum, Municipal Buildings, 1. Furnished weaver's cottage, *c*. 1800, containing spinning wheel. Bobbin winders and small carpet loom.

Liverpool. City of Liverpool Museum, William Brown Street, 3. Nineteenth-century rug-making loom. Mediterranean embroideries, Chinese embroideries and lace. Costume.

London. The British Museum, W.C.1. Textile materials in various departments.

Hornsey College of Art, Crouch End Hill, N.8. Large collection of textile designs, pattern books, and fabrics.

The London Museum, Kensington Palace, W.8. Spinning wheels, silk winders, looms, sewing machines.

Science Museum, South Kensington, S.W.7. Numerous early textile machines for the processing of the various textile fibres, also models of some of these machines.

Victoria and Albert Museum, South Kensington, S.W.7. Numerous early fabric pattern books, English and foreign, including some displayed at the Great Exhibition. Estimates with samples of fabrics for furnishing different rooms in a house, *c*. 1790. Pattern books and samples of cotton, woollen, and silk samples from the Bridewell Museum, Norwich.

Manchester. Gallery of English Costume, Platt Hall, Rusholme, 14. Crimping machine, sewing machines. Many English costume exhibits, from the sixteenth century.

Museum of Science and Technology, Oddfellows Hall, Grosvenor Street 1. Spinning wheel, Arkwright throstle frame, replica of a slubbing billy. Early and late nineteenth-century textile machinery, including cotton-opening and scutching machines, carding and combing machines, drawframes, flyframes, mule and ring frame, jacquard silk loom and knitting machine. Models of some of the above.

The Whitworth Art Gallery, The University of Manchester, Whitworth Park, 15. A few primitive looms. Pattern books from 1875 to 1896.

Norwich. Bridewell Museum of Local Industries and Rural Crafts. Silk winders, beam warper, jacquard looms, loom for weaving horsehair cloth, model silk power loom, 1844. Wool combs.

Nottingham. City of Nottingham Museum and Art Gallery, The Castle. Costume exhibits embodying lace of both local and foreign manufacture.

Industrial Museum, Great Georgian Stable-Block of Wollaton Hall. Lace machines. Numerous pattern books containing samples of machine-made lace dating from 1841.

Oldham. Saddleworth Museum, High Street, Uppermill. Local textile machinery. Period costume.

Paisley. Museum and Art Galleries, High Street. Hand loom, jacquard loom, models of a drawloom and jacquard loom. Printing blocks used in the production of printed shawls. Pattern books containing designs for Paisley shawls. A large collection of Paisley shawls.

Salford. Museum and Art Gallery, Peel Park, 5. Hand cards. Saxony-type spinning wheel. Spindles and shuttles. Looms and model looms. Early trade price lists. Mill record books. Sample books and cards of various woven fabrics. Eighteen volumes containing 1,000 textiles bought in Indian bazaars, and including muslins, calicoes, towellings, and silks. A printed tapestry on linen, 1761.

Totnes, South Devon. The Elizabethan House (Totnes Borough Museum), 70 Fore Street. Hand loom, seventeenth century with later additions. Costume exhibits.

York. Castle Museum.

Select Bibliography for Further Reading

Allen, W. G. *John Heathcoat and his Heritage*, Johnson, London, 1958.

Aspin, C., and Chapman, S. D. *James Hargreaves and the Spinning Jenny*, Helmshore Local History Society, 1964.

Baines, E. *History of the Cotton Manufacture in Great Britain*, 1835, Republished by Frank Cass, London, 1966.

Bischoff, J. *A Comprehensive History of the Woollen and Worsted Manufacture*, 1842, Republished by Frank Cass, London, 1968.

Briand, A., and Woodhouse, T. *A Century of Progress in Jute Manufacture*, Winter and Son, Dundee, 1934.

Burnley, J. *The History of Wool and Wool Combing*, Sampson Low, London, 1889.

Chapman, S. D. *The Early Factory Masters*, David and Charles, Newton Abbot, 1967.

Chapman, S. D., and Aspin, C. *James Hargreaves and the Spinning Jenny*, Helmshore Local History Society, 1964.

Chapman, S. J. *The Lancashire Cotton Industry*, University of Manchester, 1904.

Clapham, J. H. *The Woollen and Worsted Industries*, Methuen, 1907.

Crankshaw, W. P. *Report on a Survey of the Welsh Textile Industry*, University of Wales Press Board, 1927.

Crump, W. B. (Editor). *The Leeds Woollen Industry*, The Thoresby Society, Leeds, 1931.

Crump, W. B., and Ghorbal, G. *History of the Huddersfield Woollen Industry*, Reprint—S. R. Publishers, Wakefield, 1967.

Daniels, G. W. *The Early English Cotton Industry*, Manchester University Press, 1920.

Dobson, B. P. *The Story of the Evolution of the Spinning Machine*, Marsden, Manchester, 1911.

233

Eckersley, F., and Shaw, C. *Cotton*, Pitman, London, 1967.

Felkin, W. *A History of Machine Wrought Hosiery and Lace Manufacture*, 1867. Republished by David and Charles, Newton Abbot, 1967.

Fitton, R. S., and Wadsworth, A. P. *The Strutts and the Arkwrights*, Manchester University Press, 1958.

Ghorbal, G., and Crump, W. B. *History of the Huddersfield Woollen Industry*, Reprint—S. R. Publishers, Wakefield, 1967.

Gill, C. *The Rise of the Linen Industry*, Clarendon Press, Oxford, 1928.

Guest, R. *A Compendious History of the Cotton Manufacture*, 1823. Republished by Frank Cass, London, 1968.

Halls, Z. *Machine-made Lace in Nottingham in the Eighteenth and Nineteenth Century*, The City of Nottingham Art Galleries and Museums Committee, 1964.

Hamilton, H. *The Industrial Revolution in Scotland*, 1932. Republished by Frank Cass, 1966.

Heaton, H. *The Yorkshire Woollen and Worsted Industry*, Oxford University Press, 1920.

Henson, G. *History of the Framework Knitters*, 1831. Republished by David and Charles, 1969.

Horner, J. *The Linen Trade of Europe During the Spinning Wheel Period*, McCaw, Stevenson and Orr, Belfast, 1920.

James, J. *History of the Worsted Manufacture in England*, 1857. Republished by Frank Cass, London, 1968.

Lipson, E. *The History of the Woollen and Worsted Industries*, 1921. Republished by Frank Cass, London, 1965.

Mann, J. A. *The Cotton Trade of Great Britain; its Rise, Progress and Present Extent*, 1860. Republished by Frank Cass, London, 1968.

Mann, J. de, and Wadsworth, A. P. *The Cotton Trade and Industrial Lancashire*, 1600–1780, Manchester University Press, 1931.

Mantoux, P. *The Industrial Revolution in the Eighteenth Century*, Jonathan Cape, 1961.

Owen, R. *The Life of Robert Owen*, 1857–8. Republished by Frank Cass, London, 1968.

Shaw, C., and Eckersley, F. *Cotton*, Pitman, London, 1967.

Unwin, G. *Samuel Oldknow and the Arkwrights*, Manchester University Press, 1924.

Ure, A. *The Philosophy of Manufactures*, 1861. Republished by Frank Cass, London, 1967.

Usher, A. P. *A History of Mechanical Inventions*, Oxford University Press, 1954.

Wadsworth, A. P., and Mann, J. de. *The Cotton Trade and Industrial Lancashire*, 1600–1780, Manchester University Press, 1931.

Wadsworth, A. P., and Fitton, R. S. *The Strutts and the Arkwrights*, Manchester University Press, 1958.

Warden, A. J. *The Linen Trade, Ancient and Modern*, 1864–1867. Republished by Frank Cass, London, 1967.

Warner, F. *The Silk Industry*, Drane's, London, 1921.

Wignall, H. *Knitting*, Pitman, London, 1964.

Woodhouse, T., and Briand, A. *A Century of Progress in Jute Manufacture*, Winter and Son, Dundee, 1934.

Index

Aberdeen, 161
Abingdon, 162
Accrington, 48
Adel, 157
Addison, 166
Aire, River, 206
Alpaca, 205–6
Alsace, 137, 188
America, *see* United States of America
American Civil War, 126, 156
Anderson, 122
Anne, Queen, 18
Archibald, J., 146
Arkwright, Richard, 39, 40, 52, 62, 65, 73, 82, 84, 116; and establishment of Nottingham mill, 50, 59, 69, 70; and Thomas Highs, 51, 56, 59; birth of, 55; ability of, 55, 68, 70, 114; early life of, 55, 97; marriage of, 55–6; and association with John Kay, 56; and the roller spinning machine, 56–7; and his association with Smalley, 57–8, 59, 116–17; and Samuel Need, 59; and establishment of the Cromford mill, 59, 60, 114; and the water frame, 59–60, 70, 149, 152; and the Belper mill, 60, 114; and the scutching machine, 63; second patent of, 66; and use of the drawing frame, 67; involvement in legal cases of, 69; and David Dale, 69; and industrial unrest, 69–70; and the Chorley mill, 69; use of steam engines by, 70; death of, 70, 76;

Robert Peel on, 115
Arnold, A., 170
Aspin, C., 47
Austin, John, 94

Bakewell, 69
Balderstone, 18
baling, 79
ball warping, 102
balling machine, 195
Barber, Robert and Thomas, 90
Barbour, John, 156
Barrowbridge, 115
Batley, 148
batting machine, 62
Bauwens, 137
beam warping machine, 102, 211
Bean Ing Mill, 47, 121, 126
bearded needles, 14, 180, 212
Belfast, 122, 153, 160
Belgium, 152
Belper, 60, 68, 113, 114, 115
Bengal, 162
Betts, William, 44
Brunel, M. I., 180
Buchanan, Archibald, 86, 116, 197
Buenos Aires, 205
Bullough, J., 195, 198
Bulwell, 125
Bunhill Fields, 16
Burnley, 198
Burnley, James, 193
Bury, 115
Butler, Samuel, 17

Calder, River, 40

236

Ireland, 116, 122, 126, 155, 156, 160
Italy, 21–2, 26, 113, 123

jack frame, 'jack-in-a-box', 57
Jacquard, J. M., 108, 109–11
jacquard loom, *see* looms
jacquard punched card system, 182
James I, King, 17
James, Dr, 39
James, J., 105, 117, 187
James, Thomas, 49, 50, 51
Jencks, 166
jersey wheel, *see* spinning wheel, early
Johnson, Dr Samuel, 35, 38
Johnson, Thomas, 101–2, 103, 123, 197
Johnstone, 63
Jurgens, 5, 6
jute industry, 162–3, 190

Kay, James, 159–60
Kay, John, 95; and the flying shuttle, 29–31, 32–4, 45, 55, 90; birth of, 31; early life of, 31–2, 97; and the 'fixed bobbin', 33; in France, 33–4; death of, 34; other invention of, 62
Kay, John (clockmaker), 56, 59, 69
Kay, Robert, 199
Kay's reeds, 31–2
Keighley, 89, 123, 201
Kelly, William, 76
Kendal, 115
Kendrew, 157
Kenworthy, W., 195, 198
knitting, hand, 11–12; peg, 12–13
knitting machines, warp, 179–80, 212; weft, 179; circular, 180, 212; and the Dawson wheel, 180; rib, 180; power driven, 180–2; Cotton's patent, 182

lace-making, by hand, 129–31; and

the bobbinet machine, 131–4; and the lace-furnishing machine, 134
Lake District, 115
Lancashire, 50, 69, 123; industrial expansion in, 68, 115; industrial unrest in, 70, 124, 125; silk spinning in, 136
Lancaster, 136, 186
lantern frame, 66
lapping machine, 64, 87
latch needle, 181, 212, 226
Lawson, 151
Leach, E., 147, 162
Lee, James, 16–17, 18
Lee, Rev. William, 11–12, 13–18, 42–3, 179, 212
Leeds, 9, 121, 151, 159, 160, 186
Leicester, 153
Leicestershire, 186
Leigh, 55
Lever, John, 134
Lever, William (Lord Leverhulme), 125
linen industry, 116, 122, 123, 155, 156, 161
linking machine, *see* chain machine
Lister comb, 189–90
Lister, Samuel (Lord Masham), 137–8, 186, 188, 193, 207–9
Lombe, John, 21–3, 26
Lombe, Sir Thomas, 21–3, 25, 26, 113, 135
London, 16, 18, 89, 161
loom reeds, 178
looms, hand, 27–9, 99, 101, 105, 121–2; steam, 91, 94, 103; Kay's fly-shuttle, 33–4; Dutch, 89, 141; ribbon, 89; water power, 89, 91; Leonardo da Vinci's, 90; De Genne's, 90; Vaucanson's, 90, 109; Barber's, 90; Cartwright's, 91–4, 95, 96–7, 101, 199; John Austin's, 94; Robertson's, 94; Miller's (wiper), 94–6, 197; witch, 105; draw, 107–12, 139; jacquard, 105, 108, 110–12,